NUCLEAR DISASTER

TOM STONIER

NUCLEAR
DISASTER

Foreword by Gerard Piel

Meridian Books

THE WORLD PUBLISHING COMPANY
CLEVELAND AND NEW YORK

GRATEFUL acknowledgment is made to the following for permission to use the material indicated:

The University of North Carolina Press for material from *Hiroshima Diary* by Michihiko Hachiya, edited by Warner Wells (University of North Carolina Press, 1955).

United States Atomic Energy Commission for selections from *Medical Effects of the Atomic Bomb in Japan*, edited by A. W. Oughterson and S. Warren (McGraw-Hill Book Co., Inc., 1956).

Cortez F. Enloe, Jr., and *Journal of the American Medical Association* for material from "Nature of Air Raid Casualties" by Cortez F. Enloe, Jr., published in *Journal of the American Medical Association*, October 27, 1951, Vol. 147.

Portions of this book appeared in slightly different form as *Anticipated Biological and Environmental Effects of Detonating a 20-Megaton Weapon on Columbus Circle, New York*, copyright © 1963 by the New York Academy of Sciences.

AN ORIGINAL MERIDIAN BOOK

To those I wish most to protect

LYDIA
JEFFERSON
HEIDI
ANTHONY KING
FRANCESCA
JESSICA

ACKNOWLEDGMENTS

Most books do not come into being without some help from some people other than the author. Some books require a lot of help from a lot of people. This book is one of those. I am especially indebted to the following colleagues whom I would like to name individually. Their contributions ranged all the way from a casual but significant suggestion during the course of a conversation, to the critical examination and review of parts of the manuscript.

Dr. H. Afheldt, Vereinigung Deutscher Wissenschaftler; Dr. R. U. Ayres, Hudson Institute; Dr. A. H. Barton, Columbia University; Dr. R. E. Beardsley, Manhattan College; Dr. R. S. Benua, Sloan-Kettering Institute; Dr. W. M. Brown, Hudson Institute; Mr. R. Christen, Manhattan College; Dr. S. Deutsch, Scientists' Committee for Radiation Information; Prof. T. Dobzhansky, The Rockefeller Institute; Dr. V. Dropkin, U.S. Department of Agriculture; Professor M. Eisenbud, New York University; Prof. H. W. Emmons, Harvard University; Dr. F. Fremont-Smith, American Institute of Biological Sciences; Dr. E. Friedman, Columbia University; Dr. W. Goldstein, Brooklyn College; Dr. J. Harley, U.S. Atomic Energy Commission; Dr. J. Hirsch, The Rockefeller Institute; Dr. M. Hoffenberg, Research Analysis Corporation; Dr. M. Horwitz, New

York University; Mrs. J. M. Ingersoll, Hudson Institute; Dr. R. C. King, Northwestern University; Dr. H. Knapp, U.S. Atomic Energy Commission; Dr. R. Lapp, Quadri Sciences; Mr. G. LaRoche, Manhattan College; Dr. J. Laughlin, Sloan-Kettering Institute; Dr. J. Lipetz, Manhattan College; Dr. S. Melman, Columbia University; Dr. D. Michael, Peace Research Institute; Mr. I. Michelson, Consumers Union; Dr. P. G. Nordlie, Human Sciences Research, Inc.; Dr. S. Socolar, College of Physicians and Surgeons; Dr. M. Sonenberg, Sloan-Kettering Institute; Dr. C. E. Stonier, Nassau County Planning Commission; Mr. W. Thabit, Brooklyn, N.Y.; Dr. P. Thaddeus, Columbia University; Dr. T. Wang, Research Analysis Corporation; and Dr. G. M. Woodwell, Brookhaven National Laboratory.

The above list is, of course, by no means complete. There were many others who called my attention to specific technical papers or other publications, or who were of help in one way or another. In addition to the scientists and other experts, I owe thanks to Raymond Biemiller, who drew the map that appears on pp. 30-1; to Thomasina Alexander, Mary Davidson, Natalie Ellis, and Sonya Wohl, who helped in the libraries and in compiling information from other sources; and to Elizabeth Bowman for help with the preparation of the manuscript.

I want to express my gratitude to Miss Jo Ann Lieb for her persistent efforts to change obtuse pedantry into meaningful prose. To her goes the credit for editing what initially was an extraordinarily incomplete, unwieldy, and confusing manuscript. It was Mr. John J. Simon who led me to take the first concrete steps toward converting the original technical report into something that could be useful to a wider audience. I am grateful to him for this start and for his continuing advice and help.

Lydia Stonier not only helped with some of the reading, typing, editing, and proofreading, but also made the many small, and some large, sacrifices necessary to the additional care and feeding of a husband turned author.

CONTENTS

Part III   THE LEGACY

FOREWORD by Gerard Piel

This is a book about the Unthinkable. It is, by no means, the first. For the reader who has the fortitude to pursue the subject further, the appendices and footnotes herein can lead on to an extensive literature. No other work, however, presents a comparably authoritative and comprehensive account of the still-impending *Nuclear Disaster*.

Tom Stonier has not only surveyed the literature; he has also made his own original contribution to it. His study of the prospective effects of the burst of a twenty-megaton thermonuclear weapon on Columbus Circle on Manhattan Island—published by the New York Academy of Sciences for the instruction of a smaller audience of concerned citizens—constitutes the first effort to assess the physical, biological, economic, and social consequences of such a catastrophe in their interaction with one another. From the particular, Stonier has here proceeded to the general: it is plain that the apocalypse at Columbus Circle could occur only as an incident in a world-wide catastrophe.

It must be mentioned at this point that Stonier is not a professional Thinker about the Unthinkable. In writing this book, therefore, he has not had the support of Federal funds, nor access to classified data, nor the facilities of a large computer, nor official sanction on the publication of his findings. Thinkers with these advantages have had a major share of public attention in recent years—in particular through the voluminous record of their expert testimony rendered before Congressional committees. The effect of their contributions to the literature is to establish a presumption in favor of the feasibility of thermonuclear war. This involves, of course, no question about the delivery of weapons to their targets. Feasibility in this context means the "acceptability" of casualties.

These studies of feasibility bear indubitable authority. Many of them are cited in this book as the sources of primary information. Invariably, however, they exhibit the same deficiency: the shock-wave study considers the effects of shock waves independent of fire and fallout; the fallout study takes no account of the concurrent effects of fire; economic recovery is projected without consideration of the psychosocial aftermath; and so on. What they lack is the essential distinction of this book. That is the relating of the parts to the whole. Ultimately this requires a comprehension of the inextricable interdependence of life, of each human life with all others and of all human life with the skein of life from which our fabric is woven. What the subject demands, in other words, is the humanity that suffuses these pages.

Part I THE ATTACK

INTRODUCTION: The New Weapon

Even in a century marked by two "total" wars the totality of the catastrophe we face in the threat of thermonuclear war is barely imaginable. The number of deaths that could result from the detonation of just one twenty-megaton bomb on New York City could exceed tenfold the total number of fatalities that America has suffered on all its battlefields throughout all its previous history. If the example of New York City is magnified to include the entire country, with its population of over 180,000,000 and its complex and highly developed industrial and cultural structure, the consequences of nuclear war take on the proportions of an American Götterdämmerung.

The creation of the thermonuclear bomb represents the latest stage in the accelerated development of weapons technology. These weapons are the products not only of the highest level of scientific and industrial capacity, but of an attitude toward war that has been described by Erich Fromm and Michael Maccoby as the "escalation of brutality."

Retired Marine Brigadier General F. P. Henderson, reviewing the changing attitudes of war, points out that planned air bombardment of cities was most repugnant to the humane values with which we began this century but that the concept of ideological war completely altered this view. In ideological war, General Henderson declares, the enemy is completely hateful; his unconditional surrender and the utter destruction of his society are the only satisfactory objectives. In bringing this just retribution to him, one cannot show compassion for noncombatants nor spare the works of culture or production that man's labor and creative genius have accomplished. By World War II, the followers of Giulio Douhet, a World War I officer whose ideas were developed into the Blitzkrieg of World War II, were committed to the doctrine that to defeat a modern industrial nation in war, air bombardment directed at cities was necessary in order to destroy the means of production that supported its armed forces and to crush the morale of the civilian population.

The shift in attitudes and techniques is reflected in the following figures: In World War I there were 9,800,000 killed, 5 per cent of whom were civilians; in World War II, of 52,000,000 dead, 48 per cent were civilians; the Korean conflict produced 9,200,000 dead, of whom 84 per cent were civilians. Part of this tremendous increase can be attributed to the fact that World War II saw the advent of technical developments capable of destroying large sections of a city, and even entire cities.

The first time that a sizable part of a large city was totally destroyed was in July of 1943 when Hamburg succumbed to the massive bombings of "Operation Gomorrah." Four major Royal Air Force raids, involving a total of several thousand planes dropping over 7,000 tons of high explosives and incendiaries, destroyed 55 to 60 per cent of that city. An area of some thirty square miles was damaged, including twelve and one half square miles that were completely burned out. Forty-eight hours after the attack, when this area cooled sufficiently to be approached, only the brick building walls and a few large charred trees remained; no traces of unburned combustible building materials could be found. About as many people died in this attack as were to die two years later at Hiroshima.

The Hamburg attack provided several valuable lessons for the strategic-bombing analysts. First, a successful attack had to be massive, sufficient to overwhelm the defenses. More than fifteen times as many explosives were dropped on Hamburg than on London at the height of the Blitz. Secondly, the bombs had to be a mixture of high explosives and incendiaries, since it was found that explosives or incendiaries alone did not start many fires. Third, it was necessary to set fire to a sufficiently large area (a minimum of about one square mile) in a sufficiently short time. If the area contained enough combustible material a firestorm or a conflagration was almost inevitable.

Many technological problems had to be solved before cities could be destroyed successfully. Large planes were needed, capable of carrying big loads at the speeds and altitudes needed for the required distances. Defenses against fighter planes, complex radio and radar devices to aid in navigation, bombing, and the identification of other aircraft had to be developed. Problems in logistics, timing, and weather forecasting had to be solved. The solution of these problems engaged the country's best scientific and engineering talent.

Within two years of the successful solution of the problems of mass bombings, as a result of the mobilization of the world's outstanding scientists, there occurred another breakthrough: the development of the atomic bomb. A few men operating a single plane carrying a single bomb could now achieve the destruction that formerly required an air armada.

Shortly before the outbreak of World War II, Otto Hahn and Fritz Strassmann, working at the Kaiser Wilhelm Institute for Chemistry in Berlin, bombarded uranium with neutrons and discovered a radioactive isotope among the products which indicated that the uranium atoms had been split. Such was the ferment in the physical sciences at that time that Philip Abelson, a young graduate student at Berkeley, California, was also pursuing a line of research which, in a few weeks, would almost certainly have led him to the discovery of nuclear fission. Within about a year, scientists throughout the world had published nearly one hundred articles on the phenomenon of fission. All the great centers of American physics became involved.

In the meantime, committees of scientists had been formed to alert government officials to the new developments and their implications. The Navy was immediately interested, not so much in the explosive potential of uranium, but in a source of power for its submarines. Other branches of government varied in their response, but all ultimately became convinced and began supporting the research.*

The pace of discovery and problem-solving continued to accelerate. In spite of many complex engineering problems, such as preparing sufficient quantities of uranium 235, a nuclear reactor was constructed beneath the West Stands of Stagg Field at the University of Chicago. On December 2, 1942, in this reactor, man first initiated a self-sustaining nuclear chain reaction, and controlled it.

Two and a half years passed. Then "at 0530, 16 July 1945, in a remote section of the Alamogordo Air Base, New Mexico, the first full-scale test was made of the implosion-type atomic fission bomb. For the first time in history there was a nuclear explosion. And what an explosion! . . . The test was successful beyond the most optimistic expectations of anyone. . . ." So reads a memorandum from General Leslie R. Groves to the Secretary of War.

Just three weeks later, an atomic device containing uranium 235 as the fissionable material was first employed as a military weapon. The first atomic bomb was detonated at approximately 1,850 feet above Hiroshima on August 6, 1945. On August 9, an atomic device containing plutonium 239 as the fissionable material was detonated at approximately 1,850 feet over Nagasaki. Although the Nagasaki drop was somewhat off center, thereby causing less destruction than had been intended, the Hiroshima detonation was an unqualified success.†

The explosions over Japan ushered in a new era of weaponry. During the first decade of that era, the technology of the new weapon developed so rapidly that by March 1, 1954, the BRAVO shot, at Bikini, marked the beginning of a class of super weapons that dwarfed the atomic bombs used against Japan just as these earlier nuclear devices had dwarfed the conventional explosives of

---

* At one point, a committee consisting of Leo Szilard, Eugene Wigner, and Edward Teller was rebuffed by an Army colonel who lectured them on the fact that it usually took two wars to develop a new weapon, and it was morale, not new arms, that brought victory. Wigner countered with the opinion that if arms were so unimportant perhaps the Army's budget ought to be cut by 30 per cent. The group got its money.
† General Groves was most enthusiastic in his report to General George C. Marshall. When the latter chided Groves for his enthusiasm in view of the large number of casualties, General Groves replied: "I was not thinking so much about those casualties as I was about the men who had made the Bataan death march," a view evidently shared by Air Force General Henry H. Arnold, also present at the meeting.

World War II.* The thermonuclear bomb detonated on Bikini exploded with a force equivalent to 15,000,000 tons (15 megatons) of TNT and produced tremendous quantities of radioactive debris which heavily contaminated the surrounding ocean. Caught in this fallout were not only the ships taking part in the bomb tests, but an unsuspecting Japanese fishing vessel, the *Lucky Dragon*, a large number of Marshall Islanders, and some American service personnel on four atolls to the east.

The Bikini shot was seven hundred and fifty times more powerful than the explosions over Hiroshima and Nagasaki. The old-style atomic bombs, with a force of 20,000 tons (20 kilotons) of TNT, hardly sufficed to provide the trigger for the new "hydrogen" bomb. In a fraction of the time it takes to blink an eye, the Bikini shot released more energy than all the bombs (including atomic bombs) dropped in World War II. Nor did this first fission-fusion-fission detonation even approach the theoretical limit of size.† Subsequent detonations exceeded the fifteen-megaton size several fold: the largest tested thus far has been the two-stage, fission-fusion device exploded by the Soviet Union on October 30, 1961, which released close to sixty megatons of energy. The addition of a uranium-238 jacket could easily have doubled the yield of that detonation, but the uranium apparently was omitted to avoid the large amounts of fallout that would have been produced by its fission.

This large detonation in October 1961 has been the exception in respect to the relative importance of fission and fusion. In general, megaton-class detonations have derived about half their en-

---

* Actually, the world's first thermonuclear device was tested on November 1, 1952.
† The new super bombs derived their energy from not one, but three, types of nuclear reaction. There was first the old-style atomic bomb, relying on a self-sustaining fission reaction. This was merely used to achieve the temperatures of the sun necessary to initiate a second reaction, the fusion reaction. This second reaction involved processes almost diametrically opposed to the first. Whereas the first fission reaction involved the splitting of the heaviest atoms, such as uranium 235 or plutonium 239, the second, fusion reaction involved the fusion of the lightest atoms. For example, two atoms of hydrogen 2 (deuterium) might fuse to produce one atom of helium 3 and release one neutron (weight = 1). The reaction not only liberated a great deal of energy, but also high-energy neutrons. These high-energy neutrons were ingeniously utilized for the third reaction, a "fast fission" reaction. This reaction resembled the first in that it involved the splitting of heavy atoms, but in this case the atoms split were uranium 238 instead of the rare uranium 235. Uranium 238 is the common form of uranium which earlier tests had shown would not sustain a chain reaction. However, the large number of energetic neutrons produced by the fusion reaction now permitted the utilization of ordinary uranium. A uranium jacket was placed around the fusion component thereby creating the first fission-fusion-fission bomb.

ergy from fusion, half from fission. The June 1959 Congressional
Hearings on the "Biological and Environmental Effects of Nuclear
War," held by the Special Subcommittee on Radiation of the Joint
Congressional Committee on Atomic Energy (Congressman Chet
Holifield presiding), assumed all weapons to be 50 per cent fission
and 50 per cent fusion. A twenty-megaton weapon would thus
produce the equivalent of ten megatons of fission and ten megatons
of fusion. Exploded near the ground, it would release about half
of its energy as blast and shock, one third (about 7×10^{15} calories)* as heat radiation, and the remainder as nuclear radiation.
One third of the nuclear radiation would consist of "initial nuclear
radiation," primarily neutrons and gamma rays, while the remaining two thirds would be made up of radioactive fission products
(fallout).†

What happens when a twenty-megaton thermonuclear device is
detonated? ‡ First, a bluish-white incandescence flashes across the
sky, followed at once by a brilliant fireball as hot as, and many
times brighter than, the brightest sun. This small, man-made sun,
like its natural counterpart, emits ultraviolet, visible, and infrared
radiation. The ultraviolet light is discharged as a very short initial
pulse. This is almost immediately followed by a second, long pulse
lasting well over a minute, in which the heat energy is emitted as
visible and infrared radiation. Maximum heat emission occurs at
about four and one half seconds after detonation, and half the heat
is released by the end of ten seconds. As the fireball rises it scorches
the countryside: on a very clear day a twenty-megaton air burst
exploded low in the atmosphere could cause the clothing of a
person standing about twenty miles away to burst into flame; people about forty miles away could suffer first-degree burns. For a
contact surface burst, the distances are reduced about 40 per cent.

In the case of a one-megaton weapon, the fireball reaches its

---

* "7×10^{15}" is mathematical shorthand for 7,000,000,000,000,000. As a further example, "3×10^{12}" represents 3,000,000,000,000. A calorie is the amount of heat
required to raise the temperature of one gram of water one degree centigrade.
† The ten-megaton fission component of the twenty-megaton bomb would yield 1,100
pounds of fission products, which at one hour post-detonation would comprise 3×10^{12}
curies (a measure of radioactivity) of total gamma fission products, including approximately 1,000,000 curies each of strontium 90 and cesium 137. In addition, the ten-
megaton fusion component of the bomb would also yield 3.2×10^{27} atoms of carbon
14 (approximately 165 pounds) which would involve about 340,000 curies.
‡ The Holifield Hearings assumed that New York City was hit by two ten-megaton
bombs. Although a single twenty-megaton bomb would not produce quite as much
damage as two properly spaced ten-megaton weapons, the simplifications in calculations are thought to justify this minor change.

maximum size (about 1.5 miles) in ten seconds; presumably for a twenty-megaton bomb the 4.5-mile maximum is not achieved until about forty-five seconds.* As the fireball expands, it rises like a hot-air balloon. A one-megaton weapon exploded moderately low in the air will reach a height of about 2 miles at the end of eighteen seconds, 3 miles in thirty seconds, 4.5 miles in about one minute. At about this time the fireball has cooled so much that it is no longer visible. Particles of matter vaporized and sucked up by the fireball begin to condense as they reach the tropopause,† 5 to 10 miles above the earth, and they now begin to spread out, thus forming the mushroom cloud, which after ten minutes stabilizes and achieves a maximum height of about 14 miles. In a twenty-megaton explosion, these events would take place somewhat more slowly and the cloud would finally reach a height of over 20 miles.

Meanwhile, a huge pressure wave, at first traveling many times faster than sound, has spread out from the center of the explosion. Immediately behind the shock front comes the wind, at speeds initially exceeding a thousand miles per hour. The wind, diminishing as it moves outward, creates a vast vacuum, and the surrounding air now rushes in, fanning the many fires started by the heat radiation and the blast. These fires, covering an area almost forty miles across, would ultimately coalesce to form mass fires, which, if the density of combustible material were sufficiently great, would then develop into firestorms or conflagrations. The size of the area would depend on meteorological conditions; in a contact surface burst it would likely be about twenty miles across.

In a contact surface burst, a circle about fifteen miles across would mark the area in which average brick houses would collapse. Moderate damage would occur within a circle of approximately twice that diameter. However, these figures are not rigid; the degree of destruction and the areas in which it occurs is to some extent dependent on meteorological and other conditions. For example, under certain circumstances that cause the blast wave to bounce back and forth between the earth and the layers of the atmosphere, windows more than one hundred miles away could be shattered.

* The rate of growth varies approximately as the square root of the yield.
† A transition zone between the troposphere and the stratosphere at which the drop in temperature with increasing height ceases. Our weather occurs below the tropopause.

As mass fires raze the destroyed city below, fallout begins to descend from above, poisoning the surrounding countryside. One bomb might endanger the lives of people in a 4,000-square-mile area. Such a large thermonuclear device exploded in midtown Manhattan, for example, would probably kill 6,000,000 out of New York City's 8,000,000 inhabitants, and produce an additional 1,000,000 or more deaths beyond the city limits.

Further serious complications would arise if the entire nation were subjected to attack. Even before the threat of fallout radiation completely subsided the country could be thrown into a state of economic and social chaos—including serious outbreaks of famine and disease—and the ensuing shock, loss of morale, and weakened leadership would further hamper relief operations and impede rehabilitation. The effects of this disruption could persist for decades, just as would the somatic damage inflicted on people exposed to radiation. Even individuals who escape the hazards of the explosion and who are themselves uninjured by radiation might carry a legacy of genetic damage, which they would then pass from generation to generation. Perhaps most uncertain, and potentially most disastrous, are the ecological consequences, the inbalances in nature itself, which might well create the preconditions for the disappearance of American civilization as we know it.

2

THE FIRST THIRTY SECONDS: Heat and Blast

We can expect that a thermonuclear attack will produce structural damage and human injury, disease, and death in a great variety of ways and over a long period of time. For this reason it is best to consider the consequences of such an attack in terms of its immediate, intermediate, and long-term effects. The immediate effects of the explosion are thermal (heat) radiation, nuclear radiation, and blast damage.

Because of the very high temperatures of the fireball, a large amount of thermal radiation is emitted from a twenty-megaton air explosion, an amount theoretically sufficient to vaporize well over ten million tons of ocean water. On a very clear day such an air burst could ignite the clothing of a man standing in the path of the heat rays about twenty miles away. In addition to being burned from ignited clothing, a person is in even greater danger of receiving flash burns, which are caused by exposure of the skin to the heat radiated by the fireball.

In both Hiroshima and Nagasaki, burn injuries constituted the major problem in medical care; from the day after the bombing on, they accounted for more than one half of all deaths. Twenty days after the attack it was found that among burned survivors the great majority (80–90 per cent) had suffered flash burns, some (5–15 per cent) had suffered both flash and flame burns, a very few (2–3 per cent) had suffered flame burns only. The importance of heat as a cause of immediate death can only be estimated, but it is believed to have been the major cause, especially among those individuals who were close to the explosion. At the Hijiyama High School in Hiroshima, of fifty-one girls who were outdoors on the school grounds about half a mile from the hypocenter (the point on the ground directly under the explosion), all were severely burned and died within a week. However, it was found that where there was some shielding the number of deaths from flash burns seemed to be reduced significantly. At about a mile from the hypocenter the mortality among shielded school children was 14.2 per cent, in contrast to 83.7 per cent among unshielded children. Some of the children who were indoors and were thought to have been protected were undoubtedly exposed to the heat rays through doorways and windows. On the basis of these and other considerations, the mortality from flash burns in this zone was estimated to be 70 per cent.

Similarly, at Hiroshima's Kameyama Hospital, 75 per cent of the patients who received burns at 0.6 mile died within two weeks. The heat energy delivered at this distance was about 30 calories per square centimeter (cal/sq cm)*, which is sufficient to ignite almost any fiber, hence, most clothing. If atmospheric conditions are clear enough for the heat rays to penetrate great distances without appreciably weakening, a twenty-megaton explosion a few miles above the ground would produce third-degree burns (12 cal/sq cm) at 27 miles, second-degree burns (8 cal/sq cm) at 32 miles, and first-degree burns (4 cal/sq cm) at 45 miles. Slightly more optimistic figures are given by biophysicist William T. Ham and George Mixter, Jr., professor of surgery at New York University, in their discussion of the thermal effects of a ten-megaton bomb. By extrapolating from their figures, the second-degree burns would be incurred at about 30 miles (10.5 cal/sq cm). They give no figures for third-degree flash burns, but point out that those exposed to 30 cal/sq cm would suffer third-degree burns from ignited clothing. For a contact surface burst, as opposed to an

* A unit measuring the amount of heat delivered per unit area. About 4 cal/sq cm will ignite shredded newspaper; 12 cal/sq cm will ignite deciduous leaves.

air burst, the above distances would have to be reduced by 40 per cent.

William Ham has stated that an atomic explosion of nominal size (twenty kilotons), in exceptionally clear air, could produce retinal lesions in humans at distances up to 36 miles in daytime and up to 40 miles at night. More dramatic was the testimony of Colonel J. E. Pickering of the United States Air Force, who stated that in the high-altitude tests over Johnston Island, retinal burns occurred in the eyes of rabbits at distances up to almost 350 miles. These burns were very small, being the size of the image of the fireball at that distance.

Although immediate nuclear radiation is an important hazard in the case of twenty-kiloton bombs like the ones dropped on Japan, the blast effects of a twenty-megaton weapon are such that the immediate radiation danger may be ignored. Thus, two and one half miles from the explosion the dose would be about 300 roentgens,* but only those in the area who are well protected from blast, shock, and thermal effects would survive anyway, and such protection would automatically provide shielding from the neutrons and gamma rays produced by the bomb. The Communication Center of the Chugoko Army Headquarters in Hiroshima, a largely underground, reinforced-concrete building located 3,100 feet from the explosion, received approximately 2,200 roentgens. Although several of the thirty-two occupants were hurt by the blast, only one showed any signs of injury that could possibly be attributed to radiation.

In Hiroshima and Nagasaki most of the immediate deaths from blast injuries occurred as buildings were blown over or collapsed, and walls, doors, bricks, glass, furniture, and other debris hurtled through the air, crushing or striking everything in their way. Blast damage to a building or other structure may result from one of several causes, or a combination of them. First of all, there is the shock front itself, which compresses everything in its path. Thus a building may collapse not only because it is being blown over, but also because the external pressure of air and gases suddenly

---

* A roentgen (often abbreviated as an "r") is a unit of exposure dose of gamma or X radiation. One roentgen of gamma radiation would result in the absorption of a certain quantity of energy (87 ergs) per gram of dry air. A dose of 450 roentgens to the entire body would kill about half the people absorbing this amount of energy.

becomes so much greater than the internal pressure that all four walls collapse, in much the same way that a five-gallon tin can collapses when the air inside it is extracted. The pressure to which a building is exposed is measured in pounds per square inch (psi) and the greater this pressure is, the stronger the building must be to withstand it.

Immediately behind the shock front are the drag forces, which operate like a very strong wind. Thus, telephone poles and radio towers, which may readily resist the squeezing effect of the pressures from the shock front, are quite vulnerable to much lower dynamic pressures that may blow them over. Unlike the shock front, which passes by in an instant, the drag forces may exert their effect for many seconds.

The shock front and drag forces moving out from the explosion cause a partial vacuum which is filled by winds blowing back toward the center. Although these forces are negligible compared to the initial outward pressures of blast and shock, they may add significant damage to an already weakened structure. In addition to all this there is ground shock, which is similar to an earthquake and would tumble buildings in the same way. A twenty-megaton bomb exploded underground would produce a shock that would approximate the worst earthquake shock on record.

We can understand blast damage better if we take a specific city as an example. What, for instance, might be expected if a twenty-megaton bomb were detonated on Columbus Circle in New York City? A surface explosion would create an enormous hole 640 feet deep and over 2,700 feet wide. The lip surrounding this hole would be about 160 feet high.* This means the crater would extend from 49th Street to 69th Street, and from east of Sixth Avenue almost to the West Side Highway. Placed in such a hole, the seventy-story, 850-foot R.C.A. building would barely protrude above the crater lip. But this skyscraper, along with others in the midtown area, would not only have been knocked down, but would also be melted by the immense heat of the fireball.

---

* The reader should differentiate between *air bursts* (such as those set off over Japan), which produce neither craters nor fallout, but are more effective in producing blast and heat damage, and *surface bursts*, which are the subject of discussion here. A surface burst is any burst that is low enough for the fireball to touch the ground. The following dimensions are given for a contact surface burst on dry soil: depth: 800 feet; diameter of hole: 3,400 feet; diameter of crater including lip of material forced up: 6,800 feet; height of crater lip: 200 feet. A factor of 0.8 is used to convert the above figures to apply to detonations on rock (e.g., granite).

Since the crater would be deeper than any of the subway tunnels in the area—in fact, almost six times as deep as the deepest tunnel in the system, the 113-foot-deep BMT 6oth-Street tunnel under the East River—any midtown hit is likely to penetrate at least one of the subway tunnels. And because the IRT, BMT, and IND lines are interconnected in the midtown area, one can reasonably expect the blast wave to blow out the entire underground-connected portion of all three subway systems.

At this point let us envision the areas encompassed by two circles (see map, pp. 30-1): one with a radius of 7.5 miles from Columbus Circle, the second with a radius of 16 miles. At the 7.5-mile line, the shock front will produce a pressure of 5 psi * and will be followed by a 160-mph wind; at 16 miles this will be reduced to 1.7 psi and the winds will have moderated to 60 mph. The distances for these two pressures are based on data from the Nevada test site, a relatively unobstructed area, and are thus larger than those that may be expected in a city burst, where the blast wave would tend to lose energy more rapidly in the process of knocking down buildings.

At 5 psi (the pressure at the 7.5-mile circle) an ordinary unreinforced brick or wood-frame house would be completely demolished. Brick apartment houses would probably remain standing but would require major repairs, although those two miles closer to the explosion would also collapse. (Were the bomb to explode in the air above Columbus Circle, rather than on the ground, complete destruction of the apartment houses *would* occur at the 7.5-mile line. In an air burst, the 5 psi line would be a little over 10 miles from the hypocenter.)

Thus, considering the type of construction in New York City, the inner (7.5-mile radius) circle around Columbus Circle would be the zone of severe blast damage. At its outer edge this circle includes, in Brooklyn, Gowanus Bay, half of Prospect Park, the former Ebbets Field site, the Bedford-Stuyvesant and Bushwick sections; in Queens, Ridgewood, the western tip of Forest Hills, Corona, and the western edge of Whitestone; in the Bronx, Sound View Park, Crotona Park, and New York University. Only the tip of Manhattan above the Cloisters would not be inside this zone. In New Jersey, Leonia, Ridgefield Park, Teterboro Airport, half

* Throughout this discussion these figures must be understood to mean pressure above the basic pressure of 14.7 psi that is exerted on the earth by the weight of the atmosphere at sea level.

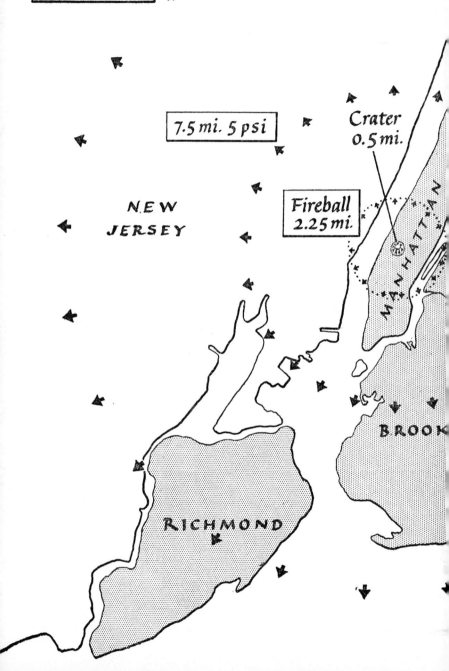

16 mi. 1.7 psi

7.5 mi. 5 psi

Crater
0.5 mi.

NEW

JERSEY

Fireball
2.25 mi.

MANHATTAN

BROOK

RICHMOND

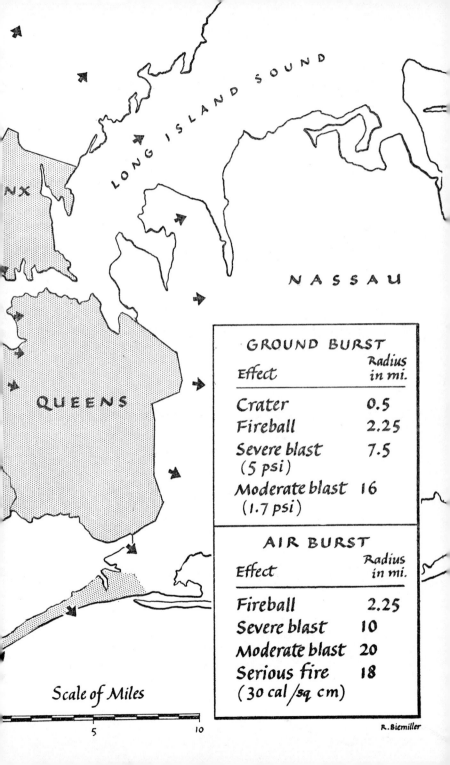

LONG ISLAND SOUND

NX

NASSAU

QUEENS

GROUND BURST	
Effect	Radius in mi.
Crater	0.5
Fireball	2.25
Severe blast (5 psi)	7.5
Moderate blast (1.7 psi)	16

AIR BURST	
Effect	Radius in mi.
Fireball	2.25
Severe blast	10
Moderate blast	20
Serious fire (30 cal/sq cm)	18

Scale of Miles

5   10

R. Biemiller

of Kearny, and most of Jersey City would lie well inside this zone of mass destruction. The Palisades ridge would probably not afford much protection since the blast wave would simply roll over it.

Although houses exposed to 1.7 psi (the pressure at the 16-mile circle) would remain standing, this pressure is still strong enough to tear entrance doors off their hinges and break them into pieces and to send window glass flying throughout the house, the force on the sash being sufficient to dislodge the frames, particularly on the side facing the explosion. In peacetime, complete restoration would not be economically practical, but in an emergency, and in the absence of fire, the house probably could be made habitable by covering the window and door openings and by shoring the basement.

The 16-mile circle around Columbus Circle would include all of New York City except the part of Staten Island beyond the Staten Island Airport and a very small corner of Far Rockaway. In Nassau County, Elmont, Floral Park, Manhasset, and Port Washington would delineate the eastern portion of the circle. In Westchester County, most of New Rochelle and almost all of Yonkers would be included, and in New Jersey, the point where the New Jersey boundary touches the Hudson River, Ridgewood, Paterson, Caldwell, West Orange, Union, and Linden would lie along the perimeter. Some destruction, such as window breakage, would be incurred by the majority of buildings up to 40 miles away, where the pressure would still be around 0.5 psi.

One more point should be emphasized in assessing the blast damage to the countryside: not all brick houses would necessarily collapse in the inner zone, nor would no brick houses collapse in the outer zone. Rather, there would be variations depending both upon individual peculiarities of construction and on the movement and behavior of the shock front. For example, the explosion of a mere twenty-kiloton bomb has been known to break windows 75 to 100 miles away. An increase of pressure and noise at great distances from the explosion results from the downward refraction and focusing of the shock rays by various air layers and from other meteorological factors. This process may be repeated when the shock rays are bounced back and forth between the earth and the air, causing damage at regularly spaced distances while leaving areas in-between intact. Thus, a New York explosion might shatter windows as far away as Wilmington, Delaware.

Of major concern, of course, are the deaths and injuries that would result from the blast of a twenty-megaton weapon. C. S. White, Director of Research of the Lovelace Foundation for Medical Education and Research, testifying before the Holifield Committee, presented four categories of blast hazards to "biological targets." They are *primary* effects due to blast-produced pressures and their reflections; *secondary* effects from fast-flying masonry, glass, and wood fragments, which may penetrate a person's body and pierce his internal organs, and from nonpenetrating, heavy falling or flying objects; *tertiary* effects from a person's being thrown to the ground or hurled against a building, telephone pole, or other rigid structure by the force of blast shock and winds; *indirect* effects due to ground shock, dust, and blast-associated thermal phenomena.*

The construction of the human body is such that primary blast effects are not likely to account for more than a small portion of the blast casualties. Although the human eardrum can rupture at a pressure of 5.4 psi, it generally requires about 23 psi. Lung damage can occur at 15 psi, but again, death is not common until 40 to 50 psi is reached. Individuals exposed to these pressures are much more likely to be killed by the secondary or tertiary blast effects, except those in protected places who may be close to a wall or other kind of reflecting surface. People in this situation may be exposed not only to the shock front, but simultaneously to one or more blast reflections. Therefore, a person's lungs could be damaged at about seven miles under exceptional circumstances and his eardrums ruptured at twelve miles from a twenty-megaton explosion.

Secondary blast effects from flying objects are a much greater hazard. In fact, for a forewarned population that has taken cover indoors, the secondary blast effects would probably be responsible for more of the initial casualties † than any other single factor. Any person within about fourteen miles of the explosion would be in real danger of being injured by flying glass. Flying concrete, bricks, or other masonry objects could produce head and body injuries up to about seventeen miles from the explosion. Even people

* Although White's testimony pertains to one-megaton and ten-megaton weapons only, the distances involved for a twenty-megaton bomb may be ascertained by multiplying the ten-megaton distances by the cube root of 2.

† "Initial" means the first few minutes following the explosion, and a casualty is defined by White as "an individual sufficiently injured to be unable to care for himself and who thus becomes a burden to someone else."

farther away might be seriously hurt by small glass fragments lodging in the eye.

Tertiary blast injury would occur as a person was lifted off his feet, sent flying through the air, and smashed to the ground or into some obstruction. These injuries—serious, and, in some cases, fatal, head and body wounds—would be incurred within about the same range as the secondary blast injuries.

FROM CITIES TO ASHES: Firestorm

The effectiveness of fire as a weapon of war was demonstrated in World War II. Structural damage caused by fire accounted for 80 percent of the total damage to cities attacked by airborne weapons. The great fire attacks on the cities of Germany and Japan were scientifically planned, with emphasis placed on target susceptibility and type and quantity of munitions necessary to produce maximum damage. Lessons learned from these attacks and from the atomic bomb attacks on Hiroshima and Nagasaki should provide valuable guidance to planners in designing measures to minimize effects of fire damage to American cities in any future war.

Thus reads the introduction to Technical Manual TM-9-2, "The Fire Effects of Bombing Attacks," published in 1955 by the Office of Civil and Defense Mobilization. It is clear that in a thermonuclear explosion those who are fortunate enough to escape the immediate effects of heat and nuclear radiation and blast would then be exposed to an even deadlier and more horrifying prospect —multiple fires, which, under certain conditions, would rapidly turn into raging firestorms and conflagrations.

There are two ways in which fires can originate in a nuclear explosion. First, by the ignition of trash, window curtains, rugs, bedspreads, leaves, dry grass, and similar combustible material, as a result of the heat radiated by the explosion. Second, by upset stoves, electrical short circuits, and broken gas lines caused by the blast. The heat from a twenty-megaton air burst would be intense enough to start many fires at eighteen miles from the point of detonation. In an explosion on Columbus Circle it is most likely that, except for the southern half of Staten Island, which is more than eighteen miles away and is partially shielded by hilly terrain, at least ten fires per acre would occur in every part of the city. Since the total area of the city is approximately 200,000 acres, one could expect well over a million fires to break out within a half hour. Assuming that fire-fighting apparatus remained intact and that people were available to man the equipment, this would offer a staggering and probably impossible challenge to a fire department that normally handles about two hundred and fifty fires a day.

To compound the danger of thousands of uncontrolled individual fires, a phenomenon known as a firestorm is likely to develop when a large area is burning. As the superheated air from the fires rises, it creates a huge vacuum, into which rushes a mass of fresh air, in much the same way that a chimney draft operates. At times, especially at the edges of the fire, this fresh air may move in at hurricane speeds. This phenomenon has occurred in forest fires, in bombed cities during World War II, and at Hiroshima. In the presence of a strong surface wind a potential firestorm may be transformed into a conflagration, which is a great mass fire entirely out of control. In a conflagration, the initial fires, in merging, spread considerably in the direction that the wind is blowing. Similarly, the pillar of burning gases, once it has been established, slants appreciably in the same direction; the higher the wind velocity, the more the pillar leans over and the closer the hot and burning gases approach combustible materials on the ground. The chief characteristic of the conflagration, therefore, is the presence of a fire front, an extended wall of fire moving with the wind, preceded by a mass of preheated, turbid, burning vapors. The fire continues to spread in a downwind direction until it runs out of fuel and may thus cause even greater destruction than a firestorm. The minimum area necessary to sustain a firestorm or conflagration is thought to be about one square mile.

Following the atomic bombing of Hiroshima, the firestorm developed after twenty minutes, achieved its maximum intensity after about two hours, and subsided after six hours, by which time it had burned out an area of four and one half square miles. Seventy per cent of the fire-fighting equipment was crushed in the collapse of firehouses, and 80 per cent of the fire personnel was unable to respond. Although no subsurface pipes were crushed, no leaks resulted directly from the blast, and the water reservoir itself remained undamaged, the water pressure dropped to zero because 70,000 pipe connections in buildings were broken.

Mr. Mizoguchi of the administrative staff of the Communications Hospital described his experiences as follows:

The fire extended right down to the river and before long flames were leaping all about us. We had no means of crossing the river and so there we huddled under the bank until that young girl from Seno who worked in the Bureau had the presence of mind to shout to us to swim for it. She jumped into the river and we followed her.

There was little reason for our having tried to cross the river because flying embers, carried by high winds, set fire to houses on the opposite bank and we were caught between two walls of fire. Fortunately . . . we were able to lie on the bottom and splash water over our heads and so escape the searing heat. . . .

Hundreds of people sought refuge in the Asano Sentei Park. They had refuge from the approaching flames for a little while, but gradually, the fire forced them nearer and nearer the river, until at length everyone was crowded onto the steep bank overlooking the river.

Soon the pine trees in the park were afire. The poor people faced a fiery death if they stayed in the park and a watery grave if they jumped in the river. I could hear shouting and crying, and in a few minutes they began to fall like toppling dominoes into the river. Hundreds upon hundreds jumped or were pushed in the river at this deep, treacherous point and most were drowned. The sight was unbelievable. For myself, I lay there in the river and splashed water over my head when the heat from the licking flames became unbearable.

Dr. Hanaoka, head of the Internal Medicine Department of the Communications Hospital, described the following scenes:

Between the Red Cross Hospital and the center of the city I saw nothing that wasn't burned to a crisp. Streetcars were standing at Kawaya-cho and Kamiya-cho and inside were dozens of bodies, blackened beyond recognition. I saw fire reservoirs filled to the brim with dead people who looked as though they had been boiled alive. In one reservoir I saw a man, horribly burned, crouching beside another man who was dead.

He was drinking blood-stained water out of the reservoir. Even if I had tried to stop him, it wouldn't have done any good; he was completely out of his head. In one reservoir there were so many dead people there wasn't enough room for them to fall over. They must have died sitting in the water.

Even the swimming pool at the Prefectural First Middle School was filled with dead people. They must have suffocated while they sat in the water trying to escape the fire because they didn't appear to be burned. . . .

That pool wasn't big enough to accommodate everybody who tried to get in. You could tell that by looking around the sides. I don't know how many were caught by death with their heads hanging over the edge. In one pool I saw some people who were still alive, sitting in the water with dead all around them. They were too weak to get out. People were trying to help them, but I am sure they must have died. . . .

At Nagasaki, with large areas of the Urakami valley only lightly built up, and with a strong wind blowing the fire up the valley in a direction where there was nothing to burn, no firestorm developed at all. Nevertheless, all buildings within one and one quarter miles of ground zero were destroyed. It is interesting to note that in both Japanese cities there were few fractures, concussions, or other severe mechanical injuries since those who had been badly injured by blast were killed by fires that swept the city before rescue operations could be started.

The firestorm at Hamburg which followed the great raids of July 1943 was even more intense and lasted longer than the one at Hiroshima. It completely destroyed twelve and one half square miles. The consulting pathologist to the German Tenth Military Defense Area in Hamburg provided the following vivid description:

Soon after the sirens had sounded—a little before midnight on a clear night—the first bombs dropped. The warning was adequate for everyone to go to his shelter or bunker, and thereby evacuate the streets. High explosives and "air mines" destroyed houses, created craters in streets and courtyards, ruined lighting and the power supply, and opened gas and water mains (no gas escaped from the gas mains). At the same time incendiary bombs started fires which spread gradually in thickly inhabited parts of town in a very short period of time. Thus in several minutes whole blocks were on fire and streets made impassable by flames. The heat increased rapidly and produced a wind which soon was of the power and strength of a typhoon. This typhoon first moved into the direction of the fires, later spreading in all directions. In public squares and parks it broke trees, and burning branches shot through the air. Trees of all sizes were uprooted. The firestorm broke down doors of houses and later the flames crept into the doorways and corridors. The firestorm looked like a blizzard of red snowflakes.

"The Fire Effects of Bombing Attacks" gives the following additional information:

Within 20 minutes after the first wave had attacked Hamburg, two out of three structural units within a 4.5 square mile area were afire. In the absence of a strong wind the interacting fire winds, started by many individual fires (augmented by the effects of heat radiation over intervening spaces), merged the aggregate blazes into one inferno. The pillar of burning gases rose more than 2.5 miles high and was about 1.5 miles in diameter. The rapid rise of hot, burning gases caused an influx of new air at the base of the pillar. This onrush of air, or fire wind, reached gale-like proportions as it headed toward the fire center. One and a half miles from the fire area of Hamburg this draft increased the wind from 11 miles to 33 miles per hour. At the edge of the fire area, velocities must have been appreciably greater, since trees 3 feet in diameter were uprooted.

The first serious danger in houses that had not been hit and had withstood explosions nearby became apparent when the lights went out, the water stopped running, and cracks formed in the walls. As the temperature increased in the streets from the spread of large-scale fires, many of the occupants of the air-raid shelters realized the precariousness of the situation, yet very few tried to escape. As time passed the air in the shelters became increasingly bad and people began to lie on the floors where they could breathe easier. Some vomited and lost bladder or bowel control. Many looked out, saw that everything was on fire, decided they could not get through, and withdrew into the corners of the shelters. Some tried to get out of the burning areas—for them it was a race with death. From the number of face-down corpses found in corners, behind rubble or walls, and in open places near tree stumps and parked cars, it was evident that the people of Hamburg had tried every possible means of escaping from the "heat that turned whole city blocks into a flaming hell."

The only safe refuge was the water of the canals and the port, and most of those who did manage to get there were completely exhausted. Their lips, mouths, and throats were dry, and their hands and faces were blistered. Many collapsed and died. Others jumped into the water, but even there the heat was hardly bearable. Those who had blankets and handkerchiefs soaked them and protected themselves with the wet cloths, but the rate of water evaporation was so rapid that this procedure had to be repeated every few minutes.

In the meantime the burned-out houses caved in. Bodies found in basement shelters were covered with rubble. Although these subterranean shelters withstood the explosions and fire, death had come to many an occupant without his suspecting it was close. Several persons were found sitting or lying in the most natural positions; others were sitting in groups as if talking to each other. In other shelters, however, bodies were found in a heap in front of the exit, a grim picture of a desperate attempt to escape. In shelters bodies were not found naked, as they were in the streets, but the clothes often showed burned-out holes that exposed the skin. Bodies were frequently found lying in a thick greasy black mass, which was without a doubt melted fat tissue. Many basements contained only bits of ashes and in these instances the number of casualties could only be estimated.

The medical aspects of these deaths have been summarized effectively by Cortez F. Enloe, Jr., Chief of the Medical Science Branch, United States Strategic Bombing Survey. He writes:

Heat Stroke. The time at which injury from heat occurs varies with several factors, such as the humidity of the air, the cessation of sweat production, and the degree and duration of heat to which the body has been exposed. In humid air, heat stroke may occur in a temperature of 60° C [140° F] and not necessarily be associated with subjective complaints. This factor accounted for the many persons found dead in rooms from which escape would have been possible and found in a position not suggestive of agony before death.

Effects of Intense Heat. . . . Police engineers in Hamburg estimated that temperatures in the burning city blocks went as high as 800° C [1,472 ° F].* Hundreds of persons were seen leaving shelters after the heat became unbearable. They ran into the streets and were seen to collapse very slowly, as if from utter exhaustion. Many thus felled were found naked. Two explanations have been offered for this phenomenon:

---

* Unidentified German documents indicate that the air temperatures actually reached almost 1,400° C (2,500° F) half an hour after the mass fires had coalesced, and that they were maintained for almost five hours. It was only after six hours that the temperatures dropped to 800° C. After ten hours the air temperature was still well over 200° C (392° F) and cooling off slowly.

the first is that flames spurted across the avenue with the speed of a tornado and consumed the victim's clothing, singeing the skin; the other is that the intense heat disintegrated the clothes without actual burning. Shoes were usually the only covering left on the bodies. When the bodies were recovered, they were not burned to ashes, but the body tissue was dry and shrunken and resembled that of a mummy. In many cases, the intense heat caused the skin to burst and retract over the elbows, the scalp, and the orbit [eye socket]. Autopsies performed on a large number of these bodies showed venous stasis [slowing of the blood flow and re-sultant clotting] with increased permeability of the small blood vessels, as well as damage to the chromatin and to practically all the cells of the abdominal organs and lungs. This result has been attributed to the inhalation of superheated air.

Beyond the local effects of heat, overburdening of the heat-regulating mechanism of the body must also be considered. Hindrance of the heat exchange between the body and the external atmosphere may be the causative factor. Many air raid shelters closed off by rubble produced an atmosphere intolerable to the occupants. Heat damage was noted in mem-bers of rescue squads who entered basement shelters where proper ventilation had been cut off for some time. Escape from overheated shelters has it hazards, too. In escaping through burning city blocks the danger is chiefly from radiated heat. The inhalation of hot air may cause severe damage to the respiratory passages, such as ulcerous necrosis of the mucous membranes. Whether this is a separate entity or part of the whole picture of injury and death is as yet undetermined.

Carbon Monoxide Poisoning. . . . Carbon monoxide poisoning is one of the chief types of injuries that the physician may expect to encounter. It is the characteristic cause of injury and death from the air in public air raid shelters and improvised home shelters. Carbon monoxide casual-ties may always be expected in flaming buildings where exits have been blocked by rubble, indicating the imperative need for adequate exits. One can not glibly endorse the general attitude that the basement of every dwelling affords relative safety. It may afford safety from blast, but if the building catches fire and, as we have said, fire is the main cause of atomic bomb damage, the cellar becomes but a tomb. It is in-teresting to note that in one fire raid on the city of Wesermünde, 175 out of 210 corpses recovered presented a picture of acute carbon monoxide poisoning. In Hamburg, it has been conservatively estimated that 70% of all casualties not resulting from mechanical injury or burns were induced by carbon monoxide. . . .*

In addition, there may be severe aftereffects, including residual lesions of the central nervous system as well as degenerative

* Other effects of carbon monoxide poisoning can be found in Table 1 in the Appendix.

changes in the heart, liver, and kidney. The Medical Branch survey
was not able to ascertain just how many survivors from shelters
and basements showed such aftereffects attributable to carbon
monoxide poisoning. Not only carbon monoxide, but also oxygen
depletion and the build-up of dangerous concentrations of carbon
dioxide, pose potential hazards; their effects are listed in Tables
2 and 3 of the Appendix. With respect to the possibility of death
from the inhalation of hot gases, it appears that air hot enough to
cause internal burns would probably cause lethal external burns
more rapidly.

It is difficult to give definite data on satisfactory means of pro-
tecting a population exposed to toxic gases and intense heat. Although many conflagrations have occurred, there have been few
actual temperature measurements. Measurements made by the
National Bureau of Standards on fire tests of two- and five-story
brick-joisted buildings showed that temperatures as high as 2,000°
Fahrenheit were reached in twenty minutes after ignition and
2,200° in forty minutes. Debris covered by fallen brick walls remained at about 1,000° for two to three days. According to one
estimate the temperature reached in mass fires probably would
not exceed 2,795°. Smoldering rubble will maintain higher temperatures and concentrations of toxic gas for longer periods than
the more impressive flaming phase of a large fire. As long as one
week after the incendiary raid on Hamburg, rescuers found large
amounts of smoldering rubble.

It has been estimated that it would take about eighteen hours
for two feet of concrete, and twenty-three hours for three feet of
soil, to transmit sufficient heat to raise the temperature of one wall
from 60° to 90°, if the other side maintained a temperature of
2,000°. Data has also been obtained from several experimental
fires, including the burning of a two-story, four-apartment building, with stucco-covered exterior, sheetrock-covered interior, oak
floor, and scrap lumber to simulate furnishings. For observation
purposes, an intake vent was placed in the center of a first-floor
living room. The building was ignited and permitted to burn to the
ground. The second story collapsed around the vent about forty
minutes after ignition, at which time gas temperatures exceeding
2,500° were recorded for short periods. As the building began
to collapse lethal concentrations of carbon monoxide were detected, the highest concentrations occurring as the roaring fire

began to die down and the building was reduced to a pile of rubble. Forty-four minutes after the building was set on fire the air at the intake vent inside the building was found to contain 3.2 per cent carbon monoxide, 8 per cent carbon dioxide, and 0.15 per cent methane. This concentration of carbon monoxide is approximately twenty times that required to produce death in a few hours (see Table 1 in Appendix).

If shelter vents were located so that they would not be covered by rubble, it would probably not be necessary to close them for more than an hour or two to prevent noxious gases from contaminating the air. Conversely, if the vents were covered by rubble, it might be necessary to close them for a period of days. This conclusion is supported by tests involving two large-scale experimental fires. However, in one of these, fatal concentrations of carbon monoxide were found five feet from the fire, and concentrations high enough to cause headaches were found twenty-five feet from the nearest fuel. The larger of these experimental fires involved only 9, and the smaller only 4, acres of burning material, whereas a mass fire covers at least 640 acres or one square mile. It was possible to enter the experimental area about an hour after the fire began, but the burned-out areas in the German cities could not be approached for forty-eight hours.

In the case of thickly populated, built-up areas in New York City, a possible solution would be to place shelters so deep that they would be adequately insulated from the heat and to provide them with an independent air supply, which would involve, besides oxygen, some device to prevent carbon dioxide concentrations from building up to toxic levels. Potassium superoxide might solve this problem, because in the presence of water it provides oxygen and absorbs carbon dioxide. To function properly, about one quarter pound of potassium superoxide is required per person per hour. In the absence of such a system, a man at complete rest in a confined space needs about one cubic yard of normal air per hour.

How much of an area would be inflamed by a twenty-megaton weapon? On an exceptionally clear day, following a dry spell in the fall, mass fires initiated by a twenty-megaton air burst over Columbus Circle could involve not only New York City, but almost all of Nassau County and irregular areas bounded by Greenwich,

Connecticut, Ossining, New York, and Butler, Morristown, Metuchen, and Red Bank in New Jersey. Calculations based on somewhat more probable assumptions (see Appendix, p. 176) indicate that, in the absence of a low cloud cover, a twenty-megaton bomb detonated two or three miles above Columbus Circle could initiate fires that would probably involve all of New York City (except for the southern quarter of Staten Island), as well as Valley Stream, Port Washington, New Rochelle, Dobbs Ferry, Paterson, West Orange, and Linden. A mass fire is not likely to engulf this entire area since the density of combustible material is quite low in some parts, in particular the New Jersey flatlands.

At this point, attention should be called to the fact that it is the contents of a building, rather than the structure itself, that make the critical contribution toward a fire. In Hiroshima, damage at stairways, elevators, and in fire-wall openings, and the rupture and collapse of floors and partitions often left fire-resistive buildings in a condition favorable to the internal spread of fires. Therefore, many steel and concrete buildings that normally are relatively invulnerable to fire spread would become completely gutted as shattered windows and demolished doors permitted fires to feed on furniture, paper, fabric, and other combustible material. Many buildings in New York rely on automatic sprinklers for fire protection, but these devices obviously would be of no value if the water mains were broken.

One of the most important factors influencing start and spread of fire in any city is building density: the ratio of roof area to ground area. The higher the density—that is, the more buildings there are within a given area—the more danger there is of fires developing into firestorms and conflagrations. The building density of the firestorm area of Hamburg was about 30 per cent, and the firestorm areas of other cities struck by this type of disaster were comparable. Hiroshima had a density of 27 to 42 per cent in the four-square-mile center of the city, but Nagasaki had a relatively low density, a fact that probably played a major role in preventing the development of a firestorm.

In comparing American cities with German and Japanese cities, one must note similarities as well as differences. For example, whereas built-up, commercial "downtown" areas in Germany and the United States are quite alike, the residential sections in most American cities consist of more detached dwellings and have a lower building density than residential areas in Germany. This is not true, however, of larger and older cities, such as New York, Philadelphia, and Baltimore, where there are miles and miles of houses that are directly adjacent to each other and that contain many backyard structures that would burn easily. The Office of Civil Defense and Mobilization states that "the conclusion is inescapable that the cities of Germany were less susceptible to fire storms and conflagration because of the combustibility of structures than cities of similar size in the United States." The cities of Japan, on the other hand, because of high building density and combustibility of structures were more susceptible to conflagration than those of the United States. However, the amount of combustible material per building (the potential fire load, or Btu content) was less in Japanese than European or American buildings. The extent, intensity, and duration of great fires is dependent upon the availability of great masses of potential fuel. Therefore, it should be emphasized that the bulk mass of combustible material is much greater in American dwellings and roof protection is considerably less than in Japanese dwellings. In other words, fires tend to start and perhaps spread more readily in Japanese than in American cities, and more readily in American than in German cities. On the other hand, there is generally more combustible material in American buildings than in Japanese buildings and hence a firestorm would be of greater intensity and duration in American cities.

The minimum roof-to-ground area ratio necessary for a firestorm or conflagration to develop is thought to be 20 per cent; the minimum area capable of sustaining mass fires is thought to be one square mile. Almost all of New York City, with the exception of parts of Queens and Staten Island, would fulfill these criteria. The built-up areas of the city certainly exceed one square mile, and most of New York City proper is more densely populated than the central portion of Hiroshima was at the time of the attack (see Table 4 in Appendix).

Only Queens and Staten Island have an over-all population density lower than that of the center of Hiroshima. Airports, cemeteries, parks, and the extensive Jamaica Bay area in Queens account for this low population figure.* However, since inhabitants of both these boroughs are clustered in districts of high population density, it is not likely that they would escape involvement in a

* In the absence of fallout, some of these areas would provide a refuge from mass fires.

firestorm. A situation similar to the one in Queens also exists in other parts of the New York Metropolitan Area. Although there are a number of natural firebreaks, including most prominently, the Passaic, Hackensack, Hudson, and East rivers, the Hiroshima attack proved that they would not be effective if fires were started simultaneously on both sides of a break. Thus, those areas of high building density that are within the eighteen-mile radius are likely to suffer from the irregularly distributed mass fires following a twenty-megaton air burst over Columbus Circle. Included would be the more built-up suburbs of western Nassau and southern Westchester counties, as well as a broad strip consisting of Paterson, the Oranges, and Newark down to Elizabeth, and a narrower strip along the western bank of the Hudson from the more built-up sections of northern Staten Island through Jersey City, Hoboken, West New York, up toward the George Washington Bridge area. In addition, even in low-population sections where there is little combustible material, fires are likely to spread via grass, brush, and woodland areas.

In the light of these considerations, the conclusion appears inescapable that the many fires initiated by the detonation of a twenty-megaton weapon over midtown New York would coalesce into several mass fires. Whether these would then take the form of a single firestorm, several independent firestorms, or a conflagration is uncertain. Studies conducted during the last war indicate that even when rain was falling during conventional firebomb attacks the fire damage averaged only 20 per cent less than that produced under favorable weather conditions. A wind velocity of more than thirty miles an hour could be sufficient to make a conflagration possible even during or following a heavy rainstorm, because once a fire is started it can readily overcome the retarding effects of moisture in building walls, roofs, and the like. Thus, even under the most fortuitous circumstances—for example, during a heavy rainstorm—a contact surface burst might ignite more than 100 square miles.

The Hiroshima firestorm covered about 4.5 square miles, and the one in Hamburg burned out 12.5 square miles. The twenty-megaton fireball, with a diameter of 4.5 miles by itself, would cover more than 15 square miles, and, on a clear day, a twenty-megaton air burst could ignite more than 1,000 square miles!

4

THE HUMAN REACTION: Fear and Flight

We can safely predict that fear would be the overriding human response to nuclear attack and its immediate consequences. This response may express itself in several forms, some of which aid survival, some of which impede it.* Overt actions are oriented toward escaping from the site of danger, but the psychological state may persist long after the actual danger has subsided. This persistent state is characterized by intense fear, flight tendencies, or a "jittery" alertness to minor signs of threats that are ordinarily disregarded.

F. C. Iklé in his book *The Social Impact of Bomb Destruction* points out that survivors of a nuclear explosion are likely to flee the firestorm as fast as they can, thereby avoiding death by heat or asphyxiation. Flight to escape from actual peril or even only to avoid potential danger is therefore a reasonable action and, as a

---

* An individual gripped by panic may exhibit two kinds of behavior. The first is a so-called cataleptic reaction which manifests itself as a general paralysis. The individual looks like a dead man, he cannot talk or move, he does not hear, though at every loud noise his body contracts. Only the eyes are alive and convey the terror. The other response is the temper tantrum. A soldier may attack his buddies, shoot at his own troops, or behave like a child in a rage. A woman shouts, heaping abuse on some innocent bystander, or wanders aimlessly about wringing her hands or crying for help. In each case the actions are clearly uncontrolled. These responses have been observed only rarely in previous disaster situations, but because a nuclear attack would elicit deep revulsion from the sight of an unprecedented number of maimed bodies, it is possible that many more people would have these extreme fear reactions.

rule, one of only short duration. This type of overt flight reaction may lead to what is often called panic: throngs of people racing to escape some danger, often in a disorganized fashion, disregarding the social inhibitions that govern normal human relations and ignoring instructions given prior to the danger. However, the term "panic" when applied to such a situation may be a misnomer. Flight, even when disorganized, is a positive, self-preserving act and a different phenomenon from panic.

The Committee on Disaster Studies of the National Research Council of the Academy of Sciences defines panic as "highly emotional behavior which is excited by the presence of an immediate severe threat and which results in increasing the danger for the self and for others rather than reducing [it]." Panic usually develops if there appears to be no alternative to flight and if people fear that they may be trapped or that escape routes may become blocked.* The resultant hysterical crowd is likely to be a menace to itself and to others. An example of this is the Cocoanut Grove fire in Boston, during which many of those gripped by panic piled up in front of the main exit and perished, but others who were led into a walk-in refrigerator in the back survived.

Panic may even involve an entire nation, as it did when France fell in June of 1940, after the disintegration of the French army and its compromised leadership. The contrast between the orderly, and even heroic, withdrawal of the British at Dunkirk and the newsreel pictures of the hordes of French civilians and deserting soldiers clogging the roads south of Paris clearly illustrates the distinction between flight and panic. A series of circumstances—a population sensitized by previous historical experience, prolonged anticipation of impending disaster, a badly guided evacuation, and a confused central government—combined to create a general panic which probably contributed substantially to the defeat of that demoralized country.

After the atomic bombings in Japan "the unexpected scope of the catastrophe resulted in panic, and therefore many of the civilian defense workers and auxiliary medical personnel did not, or could not, report to their stations." The term "flight" should probably be substituted for "panic." Although there may have been some instances of panicky behavior, in general the immediate

* Iklé considers one of the most ill-advised defense measures in the United States the placing of signs along the outgoing highways from large cities indicating that in the event of enemy attack those escape routes would be closed.

response to the explosion was adaptive activity such as digging out of the debris, fleeing the burning city, or assisting in rescue operations.

If the behavior following the atomic explosions was adaptive and saved the lives of those not physically incapacitated, behavior less dominated by fear might have saved still more lives. The calls for help that came from the wreckage of every second or third house at Hiroshima were ignored by the fleeing survivors who were generally too preoccupied with themselves or their own families to help trapped neighbors. Furthermore, the fear remained long after the immediate crisis situation. Dr. Takashi Nagai, author of *We of Nagasaki*, has described the fear that prevented him from leaving the shelter to cross the open spaces to the ruins of his neighborhood: "Any instant now there might be another great flash overhead. I was shaking with fear. . . ." Human activities were paralyzed by overwhelming, constant fear.* Dr. Nagai also points to one of the lasting consequences of the flight reaction, guilt. Those who survived had fled their neighborhoods while friends and family died. Many of the survivors felt that they had saved their own skins without stopping to help their neighbors, and they were haunted by that knowledge.

Whereas guilt is usually felt most strongly after the crisis subsides and may persist throughout a person's life, lethargy, pessimism, and general depression usually appear within hours or days. The most prominent symptoms include lack of interest in normal social activities, general apathy, absence of initiative, and abnormally low levels of energy. In addition, whether they are depressed or not, disaster victims show a strong tendency to depend on authoritative persons, particularly when they first become aware of their plight. People in this emotional state become completely passive and follow any directive in an almost automatic way. An example of this phenomenon was observed at Hiroshima and described by Dr. Hachiya, director of the Communications Hospital, in his book, *Hiroshima Diary*:

Never again would I be witness to such destruction and such a spiritless people. . . . After the *pica* [flash] the entire population had been

* It should be stressed that the survivors of the Japanese bombings did not have to contend with fallout—more important from the point of view of post-detonation psychology, they had never even heard of fallout. This meant that although the survivors were victimized by fear, the relief parties, in general, were not. In the case of a thermonuclear attack, on the other hand, relief parties would be conscious of the potential threat of radiation and would probably proceed with timidity.

reduced to a common level of physical and mental weakness. Those who were able walked silently towards the suburbs and the distant hills, their spirits broken, their initiative gone. When asked whence they had come, they pointed to the city and said "that way" and when asked where they were going, pointed away from the city and said "this way." They were so broken and confused that they moved and behaved like automatons . . . long files of people holding stolidly to a narrow rough path, where close by was a smooth easy road going in the same direction.

The immediate survivors of a disaster are also frequently so frightened or so stunned that they cannot utilize the resources available to them with the greatest effectiveness, nor can they muster the courage to conduct rescue operations. Nowhere is the incapacitating effect of fear more clearly illustrated than by the events that followed the sinking of the *Titanic* in 1912. Of sixteen hundred men, women, and children in the icy water only thirteen people were picked up by the half-empty lifeboats nearby. Only one of the eighteen boats made the attempt to return and rescue them. The others failed to lend assistance out of fear of being swamped. In boat after boat, the suggestion to go back and help was countered by the sentiment, Why should we lose all our lives in a useless attempt to save others from the ship? *

The damaging effect of fear is therefore not so much that it elicits the flight reaction, which is a healthy, normal, and life-saving response, but that it leads to a paralysis of judgment and action that tends to prevent the maximum use of available resources and thereby prevents preserving the maximum number of lives.

Fear for one's own safety is not the only psychological response to danger. Social interactions may be drastically altered during times of great stress. Violent events that threaten one's life or well-being bring about changes in values, changes that apparently do not involve substitutions of new values for old, but rather a shift in the emphasis on existing values. This shift in emphasis is almost instantaneous as the disaster strikes, and involves, in particular, relationships of an individual to his family and to the value of status and property. The individual immediately becomes concerned about his family, sometimes putting their safety even before his own. This phenomenon contradicts the more popular

* In this connection, one may question whether shelter areas designed to protect survivors from fallout would be used with maximum efficiency if those who arrived early suspected that there would not be enough room for more people.

impression that disaster tends to release the amoral and totally selfish tendencies in man.

In contrast to concern about the family, property loses its significance at the time of general disaster; loss or destruction of material goods is usually not the cause of serious grief. Social status and personal identity also lose their importance. What is significant in an emergency is not the position a person held in pre-disaster society, but rather what capabilities he possesses that could be used effectively in coping with the crisis.

Society is composed of subunits, among which are *primary* groups, such as families, and *secondary* groups, such as business organizations. Members of primary groups have daily personal relationships with each other and provide for each other's safety and welfare; the most intense loyalties are directed toward the people in these small groups. The most numerous and most significant primary group in the United States is the family. The extreme importance of the family in disaster is revealed during the threat, the actual impact, and throughout the crisis situation. During the actual impact, people try to survive and protect their families. At the time a family is threatened with disaster, wives tend to worry first about their children, second about their husbands. On the other hand, husbands concern themselves about their wives first, then their children. When, and if, the safety of the family is assured, both turn next to close relatives, then to friends and neighbors, last to casual acquaintances and strangers.

In the post-disaster period the survivors first attempt to establish contact with all immediate family members. Husbands and fathers take the initiative in looking for their families, providing for them, and insuring their safety, doing so at the expense of their other social duties and obligations. The ability to cope with a disaster situation is greatly improved once the family is reunited.* Aside from the family group, only the neighborhood and work groups have any significance for ordering behavior in a crisis situation.

At Hiroshima, the day after the bombing, the Communications Hospital became crowded with parents "half crazy with grief" searching for their children, as well as husbands looking for wives,

* In view of this one may question the practicality of current Civil Defense policies which expect parents to remain at home and children to remain in schools while anticipating impending disaster. Similarly, following attack, the urge on the part of mothers to go to their children, regardless of fallout radiation, might well cause many casualties.

and children for their parents. Dr. Hachiya, director of the hospital, describes how "one poor woman, insane with anxiety, walked aimlessly here and there through the hospital calling her child's name."

Prolonged fear reactions in World War II increased with "narrow-escape" experiences, and in other types of disasters it has been found that fear is prolonged as the future of the victims remains uncertain. Since nuclear-attack survivors would probably suffer varied and sustained threats to their lives, these fear reactions are likely to persist for longer periods of time than those following conventional bombings.*

The pattern of fear and shock may vary from one individual to the next. However, regardless of the pattern, there is always, at least temporarily, some impairment of mental efficiency which decreases the ability to perceive reality correctly. This inability to appraise properly the safe and dangerous features of the disaster environment and to evaluate realistically the consequences of alternative courses of action would seriously interfere with rescue and relief activity. The impairment of sound judgment probably would be more severe in the case of a nuclear explosion, not only because of the very large numbers of people involved, but also because a nuclear disaster involves a series of successive threats each very different in nature from the previous one. For these reasons, many erroneous decisions are likely to be made during the immediate post-attack period—decisions that could prove fatal.

---

* These physiological-psychosomatic manifestations include nervousness, excitability, hypersensitivity, sleeplessness, loss of appetite, headaches, inability to concentrate, nightmares, and in some cases a persistent dazed and confused condition.

5

THE RESIDUE: Fallout

As was pointed out in Chapter 2, the detonation of a twenty-megaton weapon on Columbus Circle would result in a hole 640 feet deep and one half mile across.* A large nuclear explosion creates this hole not only by blasting the earth, but also by vaporizing the material touched by the fireball. In the case of the Columbus Circle detonation this means that not only the soil and bedrock, but also most of the buildings and people in the half-mile area, would be totally evaporated.

As the fireball reaches the upper, cooler layers of the atmosphere, condensation occurs and in certain layers the condensed material begins to spread out, forming the characteristic mushroom cloud. For a twenty-megaton explosion, most of the material would probably condense between 60,000 and 110,000 feet. The cloud becomes stabilized about ten minutes after detonation, at which time gravitational and meteorological forces begin to dominate the behavior of the cloud particles, causing them to descend and to spread over the countryside. The heavier particles land close to ground zero, descending like a mild desert sandstorm, while

* The reader should keep in mind that only those explosions in which the fireball touches the ground, which are the subject of discussion in this chapter, produce an appreciable amount of local fallout.

the lighter particles are carried downwind. Both the heavy and light particles, containing fused fission products, are highly radio-active and constitute the local fallout. They can, of course, pose a most serious threat to life many miles downwind from the ex-plosion.

It is difficult to gain a full understanding of the biological effects of local fallout because very few human populations have been exposed to relatively high levels of fallout. There was virtually no fallout in Japan since both detonations involved air, rather than surface, bursts. Any radiation injuries that did occur were from the initial nuclear radiation suffered by those who were close to the hypocenter. Fallout accidentally injured a group of Marshall Islanders and American service personnel following the detonation of a nuclear device at the Pacific proving ground in the spring of 1954. A careful study of these victims has provided much in-formation, on which much of this chapter is based.

Fallout injuries can be divided into three general classes. These are the syndromes of whole-body radiation injury, which are produced by penetrating, hard gamma radiation; superficial radiation burns produced by soft radiations (beta and low-energy X or gamma radiations); and radiation injury produced by the deposition of radioactive substances within the body. In the last, the clinical picture would depend on where in the body the sub-stances were placed and how much of this radioactive material was deposited. In each of these classes there is an early phase, in which a person would experience acute signs and symptoms, and a late phase, in which chronic changes or manifestations such as cancer would occur. In each case the degree of injury is proportional to the dose, particularly with whole-body irradiation.

The syndromes resulting from total-body exposure in man are similar to those that have been studied in greater detail in other mammals. After large doses of several thousand roentgens or more, what is known as a Central-Nervous-System Syndrome is produced. An individual suffering from the CNS will become hyperexcitable, lose his muscular co-ordination, experience respiratory distress, fall into intermittent stupor, and will die within hours or days—doses capable of producing this syndrome are invariably fatal. Doses in excess of 1,500 roentgens may not produce the CNS Syndrome but are sufficient to produce the Gastro-Intestinal Syndrome and are also always fatal. The GIS is so named because of the marked nausea, vomiting, diarrhea, and denudation of the small bowel mucosa. Human cases of GIS leading to death in the first week are well documented clinically and pathologically. Doses below 1,500 roentgens produce a GIS of decreasing duration; in fact, if the dose is sufficiently low, the exposed individual will vomit for a relatively short time and may survive, providing the Hemopoietic Syndrome does not prove lethal. The HS involves the blood system, including anemia, and results in impairment of bodily functions due to a general oxygen deficiency; a decrease in the number of white blood cells circulating in the bloodstream (granulocytopenia), with accompanying depressed defenses against infection; and a reduction of the blood platelets (thrombopenia), which reduces the blood's ability to clot and which may be associated with the appearance of hemorrhagic lesions (purpura) in the skin, mucous membranes, and internal organs. Any of these may be, but are not necessarily, fatal. After the atomic bombings in Japan deaths from infection were most prevalent in the second to fourth week, and from hemorrhages in the third to sixth week, although radiation deaths occurred as late as the seventh week.

In order to study the effects of radiation on large populations, scientists have developed a measure to determine how much of any lethal agent is necessary to kill 50 per cent of any given population. The lethal dose of radiation required to kill 50 per cent of a human population (LD_{50}) is generally considered to be at around 450 roentgens, whole-body radiation. However, on the basis of hematological effects seen in the Marshall Island data, the LD_{50} seems to be closer to 350 roentgens for fallout gamma radiation. Among the young, the aged, and the debilitated, some people might even be killed by doses as low as 225 roentgens.

These figures may well prove to be correct for human populations deprived of adequate medical care. This means that the "biological" LD_{50}, i.e., if man were left to his own devices out in nature, in contrast to the "cultural" LD_{50}, i.e., with nursing care and medical attention, is more likely to be around 350 roentgens for a "typical" population, which includes the very young, the very old, the ill, as well as the young and vigorous. A 1961 National Academy of Sciences report points to the fact that published figures of animal LD_{50}'s have usually been based on experiments utilizing vigorous, young-adult animals and are therefore maximal, or nearly so. Young, immature animals or older animals beyond their prime of life are much more susceptible. Similarly, resistance to radiation is correlated with general vigor, for the most radiation-resistant strains tend to be longer lived and less susceptible to spontaneous infectious diseases.

Individuals exposed to radiation in the lethal range, above perhaps 225 roentgens, where some but not all will die in the first several weeks following exposure, can be divided according to symptoms and signs into three groups in which survival is, respectively, *improbable, possible,* and *probable.* There is no sharp line of demarcation among the groups.

If vomiting occurs promptly or within a few hours and continues and is followed in rapid succession by prostration, diarrhea, loss of appetite, and fever, the prognosis is grave, and all persons thus stricken will almost definitely die within the first week. Since there is no known therapy for these people, in a catastrophe attention should be devoted principally to others for whom there is some hope. Among those for whom death is possible but not definite, vomiting may occur early but will be of relatively short duration followed by a period of well-being. However, during this period of well-being marked changes are taking place in the blood tissues: many of the blood cells and other blood constituents are profoundly depressed; signs of infection may appear after a week; external evidence of bleeding may occur within two to four weeks. This group represents the uncertain cases, with a latent period of from one to three weeks with little clinical evidence of injury other than slight fatigue. At the end of the latent period, the patient may develop a number of signs and symptoms of the hemopoietic syndrome, any one of which may be fatal.* The mortality will be significant but with the appropriate therapy—good nursing care, blood transfusions, bone-marrow grafts, antibiotics, maintenance of electrolyte and water balance—survival time can be prolonged, and if sufficient time is provided for bone-marrow regeneration the survival rate will be increased. The group for whom survival is probable consists of individuals who may or may not have had fleeting nausea and vomiting on the day of exposure. In this group there is no further evidence of effects of the exposure except the changes that can be detected by studies of the blood. All defenses against infection are lowered even by sublethal doses of radiation

* For a more complete description, see Appendix, p. 177.

and therefore patients should be kept under close observation and administered appropriate therapy.

Superficial radiation burns produced by beta or low-energy X or gamma radiations do not seriously aggravate the reduction in blood cells caused by the penetrating radiation. However, with more severe degrees of blood depression, open wounds caused by the radiation burns would present additional portals of entry for invading microorganisms. Thus the chances of recovery would be diminished as a result of the combined injury.

Twenty-four to forty-eight hours after exposure to the snowlike fallout, one quarter of the sixty-four exposed Marshall Islanders on Rongelap Island experienced itching and a burning sensation of the skin. A few also complained of burning and tearing eyes. All skin symptoms subsided within one to two days, but evidence of cutaneous radiation injury appeared about two weeks after exposure when skin lesions and loss of hair became apparent. During the early stages of development of the lesions, the victims felt itching, burning, and slight pain with the more superficial lesions and severe pain with deeper lesions. The deep, foot lesions were the most painful and caused some of the people to walk on their heels during the acute stages. Some of the more severe lesions of the neck or armpits were painful when turning the head or raising the arms. The lesions did not produce any constitutional symptoms, but some, particularly those of the feet, became secondarily infected and required antibiotics. However, most healed rapidly and new skin covered the ulcerated areas within a week to ten days, although one ear lesion took several months to heal.

The deposition of radioactive substances within the body did not prove to be a serious immediate danger among the Marshall Islanders. However, it must be remembered that that was a megaton burst on coral, whereas a surface burst on an American city might produce fallout with very different characteristics. Furthermore, the Marshall Islanders were an unprotected population that was evacuated within one or two days; thus whole-body radiation and superficial burns were of much greater importance. In a larger, urban area, where it is more likely that inhabitants would try to seek protection rather than escape from the city, the results might be quite different. For example, individuals housed in a shelter in the fallout zone for a long period of time might possibly breathe in the very small particles that can enter through shelter ventilating systems. The effects of these inhaled radio-active particles are not fully known. In human beings and animals, the principal effects of radiation to the respiratory tract are pneumonitis and fibrosis; and in experimental animals it is also carcinoma. There is no reason to think that carcinogenesis would not also be one of the effects on man, despite the lack of definitive evidence at present.

In spite of a good deal of public emphasis on the potential fallout threat, the extent of the danger and the area that would be threatened is uncertain and difficult to predict in detail. As indicated above, the heavier fallout particles return to earth near ground zero, whereas the lighter particles may be carried for considerable distances by the prevailing winds. The horizontal distance traversed by any given fallout particle depends upon the height reached before descent, the size of the particle, and the wind pattern. It is difficult to predict the over-all pattern of fallout because none of these three variables can be ascertained in advance.

A megaton-class weapon has never been exploded on granite, much less on the granite bedrock on which the steel and concrete structures of large cities rest. This means that the rate of condensation, and the consequent size of the particles, cannot be predicted. Therefore neither the height nor the rate of descent would correspond exactly to fallout from experimental bursts, such experience having been limited to kiloton bursts on silicate, as in Nevada, or megaton bursts on coral, as in the Pacific. It is not even certain how much of the fallout would descend locally and how much would consist of particles so small that upon injection into the stratosphere they would become part of the world-wide fall-out.* Nor is it certain just how radioactive all this air-borne material would be. The presence of large quantities of structural materials like glass, steel, and concrete, containing sodium, silicon, iron, nickel, copper, zinc, manganese, and cobalt, could add significant amounts of radioactive substances to the fallout. These elements become radioactive as a result of being bombarded by the tre-

* The Holifield Hearings assumed that 80 per cent of the fallout would be local and would descend within two days following a contact surface burst. The 1962 edition of The Effects of Nuclear Weapons assumed that 60 per cent would descend locally.

mendous number of neutrons released by the fusion reaction. For example, if substantial amounts of the long-lived, radioactive isotope of cobalt were contained in the fallout, the radiation dose a year after the detonation would be appreciably higher than it would be if the fallout contained only fission products.

Even if the exact size and radioactivity of the particles were known, it is not possible to predict the wind pattern. A wind pattern may show simple, smooth contours, or it may have varying velocities and varying directions at several altitudes. Were a smooth, uniform wind to act on the mushroom cloud, the fallout would still not be distributed uniformly. Micrometeorological variations produced by hilly terrain, firestorms, and other phenomena would create turbulence and variations in deposition. Furthermore, fallout particles, particularly the smaller ones, tend to travel much more in a horizontal than in a vertical direction, resulting in the formation of drifts. Thus, in an area exposed to fallout, there would be patches with fallout piled up around obstructions (like snowdrifts) alternating with only slightly contaminated patches. Once the fallout has settled it is subject to "weathering," * which involves a complex interaction between the chemical species present in fallout, their varying physical form, the chemical and physical properties of the soil or other surfaces, plus the mechanical transport caused by wind, precipitation, and earth movement. One could also expect an effect on plant and animal life as they pertain to soil surfaces.†

If one twenty-megaton bomb were dropped on Columbus Circle we might expect only moderate fallout contamination, because the high wind velocities prevailing in the deep column of the atmosphere above New York would tend to blow most of the radioactive debris out to sea. Nevertheless, there would still be a 4,800-square-mile area in which unshielded objects would receive a total dose of 2,100 roentgens by the end of the second day, with an additional 575 roentgens during the next twelve days. Between the end of two weeks and two months a dose of 170 roentgens would be ac-

* Not much is known about weathering, and what is, is classified. As Ralph Lapp points out, there is an urgent need for reliable data on the physical and chemical behavior of fallout particles on soil surfaces, building materials, and surfaced roads. In the absence of reliable weathering data, no reasonable estimates can be made concerning the long-term doses to be expected from a contaminated area.
† For a more detailed discussion of the various factors influencing the fallout pattern, see pp. 178-81 of the Appendix.

cumulated, with another 100 roentgens during the next ten months.*

These figures illustrate the average dose rates to unshielded objects three feet above ground. However, the doses actually received by people and many other organisms would be less, depending on the extent of protection provided by natural and artificial shielding. Scientists measure such shielding in terms of "half-value layer thickness," which is the protection needed to reduce the radiation by ½. This means that if an individual is protected by one half-value thickness the dose is cut by ½; if he has two, the dose is cut to ¼ (½ x ½); if he has three, the dose is cut to ⅛ (½ x ½ x ½), and so on. The "shielding factor," that is, the extent to which the radiation is reduced, is then measured in terms of half-value thicknesses, so that one half-value thickness provides a shielding factor of 2 (2^1), two half-value thicknesses provide a factor of 4 (2^2), three half-value thicknesses provide a factor of 8 (2^3).

The Effects of Nuclear Weapons gives the following approximate half-value layer thicknesses for gamma rays from fission products:

Steel	0.7 inches
Concrete	2.2 inches
Earth	3.3 inches
Water	4.8 inches
Wood	8.8 inches

This means that a woodchuck hibernating 33 inches below ground would have ten half-value thicknesses of matter between it and the fallout. He would have a shielding factor of 2^{10} and would thus receive only 1/1024 of the radiation he would have received above ground. The woodchuck would therefore not face much of a threat from radiation, nor would any other animal that happened to interpose the necessary amount of matter between it and the fallout for sufficiently long periods of time.

In the case of man, the first floor of a wood-frame house would provide a shielding factor of 1.7—that is, it would reduce the fallout dose by 1.7—which would only be significant if the fallout were relatively light. However, lying on the first floor of a two-story brick-veneer house increases the shielding factor to 6. If either

* For a detailed discussion of the fallout pattern from the Columbus Circle burst, see pp. 181-7 of the Appendix.

house has a completely underground basement a shielding factor of about 25 is likely at the center of the basement. It stands to reason that if one lies in such a basement under a strong piece of furniture—a table, desk, bed, or filing cabinet covered with doors—on top of which have been piled ten inches of dirt (three half-value thicknesses), one would be protected by an additional shielding factor of 8, which brings the total to about 200. Although more protection is always desirable, a shielding factor of 200 is certainly adequate for the fallout field under discussion. A person lying in the center of an apartment-house basement that has partially exposed walls would be protected by a factor of 50 to 250. The same would be true if he was in the center of a floor near mid-height of a large building. A completely underground basement of a multistory building would similarly provide a shielding factor of 250 to 1,000; subbasements, of course, are even better. A simple one-man foxhole three feet in diameter and four feet deep can provide a shielding factor of about 40 if there is fallout present up to the edge but none inside. If an area three or four feet wide around the foxhole is kept free of fallout material, a protection factor of 100 or more is possible. This kind of emergency measure would probably be particularly effective if the foxhole were dug downwind from a row of trees or other kind of windbreak.

The preceding information will be clearer if we take as an example a moderately heavy fallout field in which the dose outside —where there is no protection—is 5,000 roentgens. The man inside the wood-frame house would receive approximately 2,940 roentgens, which, in light of the assumed LD50 of 450 roentgens, is fatal. The person in the brick-veneer house, with a shielding factor of 6, would receive about 833 roentgens, which is still in the lethal range. However, if either of these people retreated to the basement of his house, he might receive only 200 roentgens and would be likely to survive. Those persons protected by a completely underground apartment-house or office-building basement might receive as little as 5 to 20 roentgens, which is not sufficient to produce any symptoms. The man in the foxhole would receive 50 to 125 roentgens and would probably survive.

It should be apparent from the above discussion that it is possible to protect oneself from fallout radiation. However, the most noxious aspect of fallout is not that it is impossible to protect an informed population against it, but rather that fallout, or even only the threat of fallout, immobilizes relief forces and prevents virtually all rescue and relief operations. If telephone lines are down, they stay down. If water mains are ruptured, they stay ruptured. If a house catches fire, it burns down. And the injured are unlikely to reach a hospital or see a physician. For this reason, most injured persons within the New York City limits—or within any large city struck by a twenty-megaton bomb—are likely to succumb to either fire or fallout.

A prediction of the over-all number of fatalities that a large city would suffer is, of course, more tenuous. For example, if we compare a twenty-megaton attack with the Hiroshima explosion we must keep in mind not only that a twenty-megaton weapon is one thousand times as powerful as the Hiroshima bomb, but also that Hiroshima is roughly comparable in both size and population to the Astoria-Long Island City section of New York, which comprises only about 3 per cent of New York City's total area and population. However, despite these and other uncertainties (including the fact that the Hiroshima explosion produced no fallout), a casualty estimate has been made, which states that the Columbus Circle detonation would kill 6,000,000 out of New York City's 8,000,000 people, or 75 per cent of the city's population.* If the bomb were exploded during the day there could be another 1,000,000 deaths added to the number of mortalities within the city limits, because then the city is flooded with a large nonresident working population, and many city residents shift from the outlying residential sections to the commercial midtown area closer to Columbus Circle.

If the bomb were exploded in the air over Columbus Circle, there would be virtually no fallout. However, the area involved, both in terms of blast damage, and particularly in terms of mass fires, would be so much larger that it would compensate for the decrease in casualties caused by fallout. Not only would there be many more casualties from heat, blast, and fire at greater distances, but the larger the area affected by heat and blast, the higher would be the relative rate of fatalities to injuries. An injured victim might be able to walk half a mile out of a devastated area to reach assistance (even if only to be transported farther out to some

---

* See Tom Stonier, *The Anticipated Biological and Environmental Effects of Detonating a 20-Megaton Weapon on Columbus Circle, New York* (New York: New York Academy of Sciences, 1963).

operating medical facility), but the same victim cannot walk ten times that distance. This is also true of rescue operations. There is a limit to how far a rescue squad can penetrate into a devastated area within any given period of time. This means that victims in the inner zones would not receive aid in time, and the greater this inner zone, the greater the over-all mortality rate.

In general, the larger the stricken area, the more difficult it is to cope with the disaster: the larger the fraction of total resources destroyed, the less effective are the remaining resources in coping with the crisis. An entire city may thus be overwhelmed so that even what resources remain cannot be utilized effectively.

Part II   THE AFTERMATH

THE HUMAN DEBRIS: Medical Problems

Boston, Massachusetts, is noted for its outstanding medical facilities, and yet on November 28, 1942, when fire swept through the Cocoanut Grove night club, producing 500 burn casualties, these facilities were severely taxed. Twenty-four hours after a twenty-megaton attack on New York City, one could expect over 5,000,000 injured people within the Metropolitan Area.* The relief of this awesome number of wounded and sick victims is one of the most difficult problems that a bombed city would have to face.

Medical Effects of the Atomic Bomb in Japan gives the follow-

* The 1959 Holifield Hearings estimated initially that two ten-megaton bombs detonated on New York City would result in 3,464,000 dead the first day, 2,634,000 fatally injured, and 2,278,000 surviving injured. Using the newer Naval Radiological Defense Laboratory data, these estimates were revised and may be calculated to 3,240,000 fatally injured and 2,480,000 surviving injured. The Holifield calculations were based on the seventeen-county Metropolitan Area 1950 population of 12,900,000. Of these 12,900,000, 6,700,000 would be dead within sixty days, 2,400,000 would be injured, and 3,800,000 would survive without injury. Presumably most of the survivors would be in the outlying areas of Suffolk, upper Westchester, Rockland, Passaic, Morris, Somerset, and Middlesex counties. One could probably expect fewer injured and more dead in New York City proper, which would be consistent with what happened in World War II, where the ratio of the injured to the killed was about 3 or 4 to 1 among the English air-raid victims, 1 to 1 in Hamburg, Hiroshima, and Nagasaki. In a nuclear explosion, mortality is very high near the center of the blast, while most nonfatal injuries occur at the fringe of the affected area. The number of injured depends primarily on the width and population density of this vulnerable, though less lethal, fringe.

ing report of the destruction of medical facilities after the attacks on Hiroshima and Nagasaki:

In Hiroshima most of the medical facilities were in the devastated area, and the larger part of them were extremely vulnerable to blast and fire; consequently casualties were heavy. Ninety per cent of the 200 to 300 physicians were killed or injured, and at least 60 were killed outright. About 60 physicians were able to give medical care despite their injuries. Over 90 per cent of the 1,800 nurses were casualties. . . . Many of the injured nurses were able to work, but the shortage of trained personnel was so grave that many untrained volunteers had to be pressed into service.

In Nagasaki most of the medical personnel were in the Medical College and the University Hospital, which were within 0.5 mile of the hypocenter and were almost completely destroyed. Of the 20 faculty members at the college, 12 were killed and 4 were injured; 600 of the students were killed and most of the rest were injured. At the University Hospital 80 per cent of the occupants were killed or fatally injured. Nearly one-half of the medical practitioners in the city were killed or seriously injured. Three months after the explosion only one-half of the 240 physicians in the city prior to the bombing were working.

Almost every hospital in Hiroshima within 1 mile of the hypocenter was so severely damaged that it could not function as a hospital. Only 3 of the 45 civilian hospitals were usable. . . . The Shima Surgical Hospital, a wood and brick building 100 feet from the hypocenter, was collapsed by blast and burned; all the occupants were killed. The Red Cross Office Building at 700 feet was severely damaged by blast and was gutted by fire. The mortality was 100 per cent. Two large army hospitals, which were built of wood and were located at about 600 yards, collapsed and burned. Four-fifths of the personnel and all the 1,150 patients were reported killed. The Tada Hospital, which was part concrete and part wood and was located at 900 yards, was demolished. The mortality was nearly 100 per cent.

The largest and most modern hospitals in Hiroshima were the Red Cross Hospital and the Hiroshima Communications Department Hospital. . . . Both of these buildings remained standing but were so badly damaged that they could function only as treatment stations, outpatient clinics, and shelters for the severely wounded. The casualty rate in each hospital was approximately 90 per cent. Nearly all the instruments, apparatus, and supplies were destroyed or made useless. . . .

The Communications Department Hospital found its operating room virtually outdoors following the blast. By the end of the day of the explosion, 400 people had been given immediate care, and approximately 1,000 cases were handled by this hospital during the emergency period. Careful records were kept of 150 patients, and about three weeks after the bombings, on August 29, autopsies were performed in a makeshift autopsy room. An outpatient department was established and was maintained until November 15.

The Communications Hospital was located about a mile northeast from ground zero, that is, within the firestorm zone. Although the second floor of the hospital was gutted by fire, two fortuitous circumstances saved part of the hospital and its staff from complete destruction: the water mains entered the building from the north, so that the water supply remained intact; and the hospital was surrounded by sufficient open spaces so as to become "an oasis in a desert of fire."

The director of the hospital, Dr. Michihiko Hachiya, had expected Hiroshima to be subjected to heavy attacks—although he had no inkling that the attack might be atomic—and had ordered all inpatients evacuated. Consequently, at the time of the bombing the hospital was practically empty and those staff members who had not been killed or severely injured were able to devote their attention to the atomic casualties. Nevertheless, the burden placed on the hospital was overwhelming, as is evident from Dr. Hachiya's description: "Instruments, window frames, and debris littered the floor. The walls and ceilings were scarred and picked as though someone had sprinkled sesame seeds over their surfaces. Most of the marks had been made by slivers of flying glass but the larger scars had been caused by hurtling instruments and pieces of window casements. . . . I saw nothing that was not broken or in disorder."

To Dr. Hachiya, himself badly hurt with over forty wounds, it seemed that in the space of one night the patients "came as an avalanche and overran the hospital." The majority were badly burned; all were critically ill. Many had been near the heart of the city and in their efforts to flee had managed to get only as far as the Communications Hospital before their strength failed. Others, from closer by, came because this building, standing alone where all else was destroyed, represented shelter and a place of refuge. The hospital could not offer very much more than that.

Medical Effects of the Atomic Bomb in Japan states that "the methods adopted for treating casualties were far below standard because of the shortage of supplies and equipment and the extraordinary demands made on crippled staffs. In the first week after the Hiroshima bombing, burns received no more than ointments and salt-water compresses. Wounds were often not even dressed."

Dr. Hachiya's description of the conditions in his hospital is vivid:

Patients who could not walk urinated and defecated where they lay. Those who could walk would feel their way to the exits and relieve themselves there. Persons entering or leaving the hospital could not avoid stepping in the filth, so closely was it spread. The front entrance became covered with feces overnight, and nothing could be done for there were no bedpans and, even if there had been, no one to carry them to the patients.

Disposing of the dead was a minor problem, but to clean the rooms and corridors of urine, feces and vomitus was impossible.

The people who were burned suffered most because as their skin peeled away, glistening raw wounds were exposed to the heat and the filth. This was the environment patients had to live in.

To make matters worse, a few days later the flies returned. Dr. Hachiya relates:

Around the hospital entrances were thousands of flies and each step one took caused them to rise in black swarms. The noise of their wings was terrific. Here and there they formed small black mountains. Poking with a stick I uncovered a denuded fish bone and beneath it discovered a mass of white maggots. As soon as I removed the stick the bone became black with flies again. . . . They were all around the hospital, inside and out, and there was nothing we could do. With the recent weather and the filth, flies had increased to an appalling degree.

Conditions were not as desperate at all medical facilities. At Nagasakai, the Shinkozen Medical Aid Hospital was established in a school building. The staff was assisted by various medical-aid groups for three days, after which naval medical detachments from Sasebo and Hariojima took full charge. This unit cared for 9,000 outpatients and 800 inpatients. There were 350 deaths. Nearby naval hospitals cared for 2,280 patients, with a mortality of 23 per cent. During the first few days fifteen aid stations were in operation and stations were later established in outside communities. Almost 40,000 people were treated in aid stations and hospitals during August. The over-all mortality was 7.3 per cent. At Hiroshima, two military hospitals were established outside the devastated area to replace the two that were destroyed, and additional military officers were assigned to them. One of these hospitals treated 3,500 casualties during the first week, with a mortality of 8.3 per cent.

Nevertheless, *Medical Effects of the Atomic Bomb in Japan* concludes that the treatment given injured survivors "probably had no significant effect in reducing the mortality rate." The proper administration of fluids, plasma, plasma volume expander, whole blood, antibiotics, and other chemotherapeutic agents, along with *débridement* of wounds and adequate cleanliness and nursing care would have considerably reduced the number of deaths. "However, even with these measures it is doubtful whether more than 5 to 10 per cent of the deaths from all injuries could have been prevented." *

According to a RAND Corporation report, it is fairly certain that there would be serious shortages of all kinds of medical supplies and facilities following a nuclear attack. This problem was demonstrated in Germany after the massive aerial bombings of World War II damaged many of the medical-supply industries. However, by itself this was not sufficient to interfere seriously with the production of the most essential supplies. The deciding factor proved to be the disruption of transportation, which made it increasingly difficult to obtain hypodermic needles, scalpels, scissors, and bandages and caused criticial shortages of heart stimulants, narcotics, analgesics, and anesthetics. There was one instance, in May 1945, in which both military and civilian hospitals near Flensburg were entirely without anesthetics, a shortage due more to transport difficulties than to lack of production.

These factors, coupled with a shortage of certain imported raw materials and of skilled manpower, forced Professor Karl Brandt, the chief of German medicine, to report to Hitler on April 2, 1945, that 20 per cent of all essential medical items throughout Germany had been destroyed, that 40 per cent of those in stock were intact or only partially damaged and would last two months, and that the remainder would maintain the supply for four additional months *provided* transportation could be restored. If these conditions could

* Ten per cent of the nation's 27,300,000 fatally injured envisoned by the 1959 Holifield Hearings would mean over 2,700,000 people saved. This is a million more than the total number of deaths from all causes in the United States in 1960.

not be met, Brandt informed the Führer, then the civilians and Armed Forces could no longer be provided with even the barest medical essentials.*

A detailed analysis of the potential medical consequences of thermonuclear war was published by a group of Boston scientists and physicians in the May 31, 1962, issue of the *New England Journal of Medicine*. In assessing the physician's role in the post-attack period, one article points out that 85 per cent of Massachusetts' physicians live within the areas designated as targets by the 1959 Holifield Hearings. Even with a series of optimistic assumptions, following the Holifield attack there would be a ratio of approximately 1,700 acutely injured persons to each functioning physician in the Boston area, and about 1,000 injured per physician in Massachusetts as a whole.

The authors point to the consequences of this ratio: if the physician were to spend only ten minutes diagnosing and treating each patient, and if he worked twenty hours every day, it would require eight to fourteen days before every injured person could be seen for the first time. This assumes that fallout is nonexistent or does not interfere with the physician's activity, because with fallout there would be *no* functioning physicians outside shelters in the immediate post-attack period. However, "the injured-to-physician ratio will be considerably improved two weeks or more later, when physicians emerge from their shelters, since large numbers of the injured will have died in the interim."

It follows that many, if not most, of the injured would receive no medical aid. Therefore, many of those injured who might survive with adequate medical care would die. In fact, just as in Hiroshima, most of the fatally injured persons would never see a physician, even for the simple administration of narcotics.

Not only the lives of those with serious injuries, but even of those with minor injuries, may be in grave jeopardy. Untreated burn wounds more severe than first degree always become infected. In Germany, the great increase in tetanus associated with burns proved surprising to the authorities. The problem was of sufficient magnitude to warrant a directive to administer tetanus antitoxin to every case of burns. The complications of blast injuries at Hiroshima and Nagasaki were usually associated with infection and

---

* Hitler made no reply and Brandt withdrew from the conference room, only to be arrested subsequently and condemned to death as a defeatist and a traitor.

slow healing. Wounds from flying fragments, although usually small, posed a serious medical problem because of their depth and multiplicity. The high rate of infection could often be attributed to inadequate care.

Exposure to radiation can significantly aggravate even minor injuries. Cells of tissues exposed to sublethal doses of radiation frequently are no longer capable of dividing. The mean lethal dose for a variety of human cell types is around 100 roentgens, which not only incapacitates the rapidly dividing cells of blood-forming organs, necesary for maintaining general health and fighting infections, but also slows down normal wound-healing processes. The First Military Hospital in Tokyo reported that in those patients who had signs of radiation injury the healing of wounds was prolonged.* The significant point is that small doses of radiation alone are usually not serious, nor are minor injuries and even some major ones. But when these two factors are combined, they can cause permanent disability and even death.

The National Damage Assessment Center estimated that ninety days after an attack survivors would have received an average dose of 110 roentgens. Although they give no figures for injured survivors, the average for noninjured was 60 roentgens. In the case of the Holifield attack, it appears that injured survivors would receive an average dose of 375 roentgens.† This radiation dose alone might kill approximately half the exposed population.

Certainly those with minor infected injuries could be saved readily, in spite of radiation effects, by the simple administration of antibiotics. But, as Representative Holifield complained, our emergency supplies of medicines, plasma, etc., are not only inadequate to begin with, but are stored for the most part in flammable buildings within probable target areas. Even storing supplies in nontarget areas poses many problems: antibiotics have a finite life, as do antitoxins (tetanus antitoxin has an expiration date of

* "The granulation tissue became anemic and edematous. It bled easily or became dry because of unusual decrease of secretions. The borders of the wound were undermined; growth of granulation tissue stopped, and no tendency to heal was shown. In other cases the wound enlarged gradually until death. In patients who survived, the granulation tissue improved again following recovery from radiation effect."
† This figure is obtained on the basis of one witness's testimony of 41,800,000 dead, 17,200,000 injured, out of a total population of 150,700,000. This means that almost 91,000,000 Americans would remain uninjured. If they received an average of 60 roentgens, and the over-all average was 110 roentgens, then the 17,200,000 injured survivors must have received an average of 375 roentgens. Hardin Jones takes a more pessimistic view and estimates for all survivors an average dose of 300 roentgens within the first week and an additional 100 roentgens during the first year.

three years) and other supplies. Narcotics, one of the most essential groups of drugs in the case of seriously injured casualties, pose particular difficulties in handling and storage.

Drs. Sidel, Geiger, and Lown, in their article in the *New England Journal of Medicine,* state that $500,000,000 worth of medical supplies, if kept up to date and if available at times of emergency (i.e., no transportation breakdown), would be sufficient to treat 5,000,000 casualties. As these authors point out, the 1959 Holifield estimate predicted 40,000,000 injured.* Nor would the medical-supply issue be a short-range problem. Many pharmaceutical houses have their warehouses, offices, and factories in potential target areas, and even those companies that could maintain production would have difficulty in distributing their supplies because of wide-spread destruction of transportation facilities.

Needless to say, those people with chronic ailments that require a continuous supply of some medication—for example, a diabetic who cannot survive without insulin—might also become casualties even though they were not injured directly by the explosion.

In addition to the lack of medical facilities and the debilitating effect of radiation, an individual with any type of injury (not necessarily caused by the initial explosion) might be at a tremendous disadvantage in combatting infection, because a large segment of the population in and near a target area would be under considerable personal and collective stress. Malnutrition, excessive fatigue, emotional stress, including hysteria, may greatly complicate recovery from only minor injuries.

* With the revisions introduced by the Naval Radiological Defense Laboratory data, the total estimate came to 27,300,000 fatally injured, 18,800,000 surviving injured (and 19,700,000 killed the first day) out of a population of 150,700,000. In the 1960 Holifield Hearings, Leo Hoegh, Director of the Office of Civil and Defense Mobilization, testified that at that time the medical stockpiles amounted to $212,000,000, that he expected additional supplies from neighborhood druggists during an emergency, and that the program was aiming to sustain 5,000,000 casualties for six months.

THE STRUGGLE TO RECOVER: Water, Housing, and Food

Next to medical problems, the most serious immediate challenges to those who survive the direct bomb effects are the problems of water supply, housing, and food.

WATER

The destruction of water supplies following nuclear attack may be brought about by one of several events: blast and fire may seriously damage the physical plant itself by destroying water towers, clogging pipes with debris, and rupturing mains. At Nagasaki, the Urakami district was totally without water because of five major breaks in buried pipes. Six additional breaks occurred, four of them at bridges, and about 5,000 house-service pipes were broken by the collapse of homes exposed to blast, fire, or both. The damage in Hiroshima was even greater, with an estimated 70,000 breaks.

Water supplies may also become temporarily unusable as a result of heavy fallout contamination. In Westchester County, for example, about 90 per cent of the population uses water from open surface sources, and if fallout were fairly heavy, this water would not be fit even for emergency consumption for days or possibly weeks.

It would probably be acceptable for emergency use thereafter, because fission products in fallout appear to be in an insoluble form, and tend to be removed by sedimentation and filtration.* However, even this "uncontaminated" water might not be entirely safe, since it could still produce considerable long-term biological damage, particularly from radioactive iodine. Ground water supplies, on the other hand, would probably not become appreciably contaminated, because of sedimentation and natural filtration by soils and rock. Furthermore, the rate of movement of water in the ground is very slow, and the resulting "hold-up" time permits considerable decay of the radioactivity. Chemical processes such as sorption also tend to reduce fallout materials in solution.†

Water may also become unusable because of loss of power required to maintain the supply system. Whereas damage to the physical plant results in immediate effects (which might be repaired later), and fallout may temporarily deprive communities of potable water, the loss of power would probably not affect a community for some weeks, or months, depending on local fuel supplies. The fuel problem might not be too serious if transportation were repaired in time to replenish dwindling stocks. However, if the power plants and a sufficient part of the interlocking power system and hydroelectric dams have been destroyed so as to inactivate the system immediately, and if the nation has been hit so hard that it remains prostrated for a period of months, then the power failure could be the most serious and long-lasting threat to the water supplies of a community.

The Jamaica Water Supply Company, which supplies about 600,000 people in Jamaica, Queens, and the Floral Park area of Nassau County, is a case in point. Because it is located at the eastern edge of the moderate-damage zone, it is possible that some parts of the system might remain operative, and since it derives its water from wells and almost all its storage tanks are closed, fallout contamination would probably not be a problem. (The main threat from fallout is that it would prevent or inhibit repair work.) However, electric power *is* required to pump water from the seventy-five or so wells, which vary in depth from 60 to 727

---

* See page 187 of Appendix for calculations on which this estimate is based.
† The ability of soil particles to adsorb soluble radioisotopes suggests that a simple procedure for the decontamination of drinking water would consist of passing water through a column of clean soil, possibly followed by sterilization of the water either by boiling or with household bleach.

feet below the surface, and for the booster pumps, which force purified water either into storage or directly into the mains for distribution at required pressures. Lack of electric power would therefore make the entire system inoperative. All the suburban areas on Long Island are particularly susceptible to a breakdown of transportation facilities, and hence, shortages of fuel supplies and power. Therefore the considerations made for the Jamaica Water Supply Company are equally applicable for the rest of the Nassau-Suffolk area, and conclusions for it may be applied with a reasonable degree of accuracy to most other large urban and suburban areas in the United States.

HOUSING

As for what we may expect to happen to housing, C. K. Shafer, Director of the Meteorological Office of the Office of Civil and Defense Mobilization, testifying before the Holifield Hearings of June 1959, stated that given the attack assumptions of that hearing,* about 45 per cent of the nation's dwelling units would be damaged by blast and fire. Out of an assumed 46,100,000 dwelling units in the United States, 11,800,000 would be severely damaged, 8,100,000 would be moderately damaged, and 1,500,000 slightly damaged. In addition, 500,000 dwellings, outside the areas of blast damage, would be affected by fallout intensities so high that they would have to be evacuated and abandoned for a year, 2,100,000 dwellings would have to be abandoned for several months, and 10,400,000 could be made available for living sixty days after the attack, but only if major decontamination efforts were undertaken. Thus the inhabitants of all but 11,700,000 dwelling units would not be able to use their homes for a minimum of two months, and even these 11,700,000 would not all be exempt from serious radiation problems.

If a twenty-megaton bomb were detonated on or over Columbus Circle, it is highly unlikely that more than a few, if any, of New York City's approximately 2,500,000 dwelling units would provide adequate shelter for survivors, even if everything were not consumed by fires. It is difficult to assess the damage in the more distant suburbs. Window breakage and other moderate blast-induced destruction could occur even as far away as forty miles.

* A total of 275 megatons to the Northeast from Washington to Boston, and a total of 1,446 megatons to the entire country.

The suburbs might also be threatened by substantial local fallout, not only from the twenty-megaton bomb, but also from weapons aimed at Brookhaven National Laboratory and Suffolk County Air Force Base at the eastern end of Long Island, and from bombs dropped along the Connecticut Valley, West Point, New Jersey, and eastern Pennsylvania.

Even those lucky home dwellers spared all other calamities might find that without fuel supplies their homes were inadequate during severe winter weather. The breakdown of the transportation system would certainly result in shortages or possibly even a total lack of fuel supplies. Thus one might expect an increase in deaths from exposure, either by itself or in combination with other bomb-incurred incapacitations.

FOOD

It seems inevitable that food shortages, perhaps very serious food shortages, would develop following a nuclear attack. A city subjected to a nuclear explosion would be faced with the destruction of one of its most vital industries—the processing, storing, and distributing of food—the crippling or total demolition of warehouses, wholesale and retail outlets, processing plants such as bakeries, dairies, and slaughterhouses, along with transportation and distribution facilities. The situation would be more hopeful for suburban residents if they could be assured a local food supply. However, in the case of a ground burst, outlying areas might be inundated with fallout, so that a farmer on Long Island, for example, would probably not be able to work his land for several weeks and would have at least some fallout-contamination problem for over a year. Besides the areas contaminated with heavy fallout, there would still be places where fallout might be less serious but still sufficient to make the food produced there unusable.

This does not necessarily mean that there would be no food available whatsoever. In addition to food stored in undestroyed areas, any crop already harvested and covered enough to prevent direct contact with the fallout could probably be salvaged. Similarly, animals killed by fallout radiation could also be utilized for food if appropriate care were taken to avoid certain organs and not contaminate the edible parts. Animals exposed to several hundred, or even a thousand, roentgens do not die until several days later, when radiation doses may have subsided to a level permitting some human activity.

Fallout radioactivity can contaminate food in a number of ways. It may settle as rain or dust on living vegetation or on the dead organic material and humus above the mineral soil. It may also, of course, enter the mineral soil directly or through the ground water, but actually most of the fallout radioactivity in plants appears to be derived from radioisotopes directly assimilated from fallout particles deposited on the leaves and shoots of the plants. The material in the soil may be picked up by the plant roots, which pass the fallout into the plant shoots. The vegetation may then be eaten by herbivores, which in due time may be eaten by predatores. Ultimately both animals and plants die, returning to the soil, thereby forming part of the dead organic material, or litter. The litter in turn is converted into humus by earthworms, snails, and microorganisms such as molds, which decompose the organic material. Through this cycle the radioisotopes originally incorporated into plants may once again enter the mineral soil. The litter organisms also may be eaten by predatores, or, as they themselves die and decompose, contribute to the humus. These cycles and subcycles may go on for generations.

One such cycle, studied at White Oak Lake at Oak Ridge, Tennessee, showed that insects contained about as much radioactive strontium as they did radioactive cesium, but that these two radioisotopes behaved very differently in the food chain. The plants failed to accumulate cesium from the soil, but the insects absorbed it from the plants, whereas strontium was accumulated by the plants but not by the insects.* Thus, a small amount of radioactive material in one step in the food chain may be multiplied many times as a result of accumulation by organisms later on in the chain. Conversely, radioactivity may also be diminished as it moves along the food chain.

* Although the soil contained 7,300 picocuries of cesium 137 per gram of dry weight, the leaves of plants growing in this soil contained only 180 picocuries per gram. Insects feeding on these leaves were found to contain 87 picocuries per gram, while predaceous insects feeding on the herbivorous insects contained about the same amount (81 picocuries per gram). The cycling of radioactive strontium was of a very different pattern. Whereas the soil contained 360 picocuries of strontium 90 per gram of dry weight, the leaves of plants contained almost three and one half times as much (1,200 picocuries per gram), indicating a preferential uptake and accumulation of strontium by the plants. The herbivorous insects feeding on the leaves contained less than one tenth the amount found in the leaves (91 picocuries per gram), since they rapidly eliminated the ingested strontium. The predaceous insects who ate the herbivorous insects had about the same concentration (81 picocuries per gram).

With the passage of time, deposited radioactive isotopes are less likely to enter the food chain. Detailed analysis of the soil in areas subjected to fallout from test shots showed that strontium-90 soil levels remained almost constant for a year or more, but in spite of the rather constant soil levels, sharp drops in the strontium-90 jack-rabbit bone concentrations were observed in one area in 1955, and in another area in 1961.

The cycling of radioisotopes also takes place in the marine environment. For example, a marine microorganism living in radioactive sea water formed during an underwater nuclear test concentrated the radioactivity by a factor of 5,000 within ninety hours. Another marine microorganism, fed a combination of radioactive strontium and its decay product, radioactive yttrium, was able to concentrate the radioactivity from 6,000 to 25,000 times. Because these microorganisms are eaten by shrimps, clams, and other shellfish, which are in turn eaten by larger animals, the accumulation of isotopes may result in further concentration as a given isotope moves along the food chain. Although our understanding of events higher up in the food chain is still incomplete, it seems that elements such as copper, manganese, nickel, and zinc tend to be concentrated in the internal organs of certain food fishes, and that calcium and strontium tend to concentrate in the hard parts of these fishes.

Studies on the distribution of radioisotopes in the Marshall Islands five years after the BRAVO shot showed that the principal radioisotopes in marine organisms were radioactive zinc, cobalt, and manganese, created by neutron induction. The land organisms were contaminated primarily with the long-lived fission products cesium 137 and strontium 90. Twelve radioisotopes were detected in the Marshall Islands soil, but strontium 90, cesium 137, and antimony 125 were the most common. Corals and coralline algae contained some stronium 90, while the principal radioisotope in the marine algae was cerium 144. Ninety per cent or more of the radioactivity of the land plants derived from cesium 137, the remainder from strontium 90. This is an unusual situation and is due to the low potassium content of the Marshall Islands soil. Undoubtedly this accounts for the fact that in 1961 these islanders' body burden of cesium 137 was three hundred times that of the United States medical team sent to survey them. Similarly, the hundredfold increase in the body burden of zinc 65 exhibited by the islanders is attributable to the important role of fresh fish in their diet.

Thus man, like his fellow creatures, is affected by events in the food chain. In some instances, metabolic barriers prevent the radioactive material from reaching locations in the body where it may cause damage, depending on the behavior of the substance in the food chain or in man's system. For example, although the elements that belong to the rare-earth group are common fission products, their absorption from the intestinal tract is so small in man and animals that they are not a significant hazard to man. Any residual uranium or plutonium not fissioned would likewise be poorly absorbed. However, once absorbed, such radionuclides could also pose serious hazards.

Ralph Lapp has pointed out that a 7,500-megaton attack on the United States could so contaminate farm land with strontium 90 that it would be virtually impossible to grow any acceptable food. Lapp assumed that 40 per cent, or 3,000 megatons, of the total weapon yield would be local fallout; deposited uniformly, this would contaminate the countryside to a level of one kiloton per square mile. Although a good deal of the continental United States's 3,000,000 square miles is not used for food production, Lapp points out that food raised on land contaminated to this degree would result in the presence of strontium 90 in human bone several times the 2,000 strontium units acceptable for high-risk industrial personnel.

The biological effects of this contamination are difficult to predict because of many uncertainties. However, we can make some estimates on the basis of nuclear testing, using a factor of about 5,000 * to project the level of food contamination from fallout from weapons testing (up to 1961) to the fallout field that could follow an attack on the scale suggested by Lapp. According to a 1962 report of the Federal Radiation Council, the risk to an individual of developing bone cancer from all tests through 1961 was about one in 300,000; the risk of developing leukemia, about one in 100,000. Thus, if one assumes a linear relationship, and if the factor of 5,000 is valid, survivors eating food contaminated to such high levels would incur a risk of 5,000 in 300,000 for bone

* See Appendix, page 188, for calculations on which this factor is based.

cancer, and 5,000 in 100,000 for leukemia. In other words, it is not unlikely that about 2 per cent of the population would develop bone cancer, and 5 per cent would develop leukemia.

These estimates assume, on the one hand, that no efforts are made to decontaminate the food, and, on the other hand, that the population has not been exposed to external radiation from fallout in the environment. Moreover, the calculations assume that the surviving population would be able to maintain its pre-attack dietary standards. It is because of the high consumption of meat and milk, with a much more favorable (low) strontium-to-calcium ratio, that human bone contamination in the United States has maintained levels not very much higher than many areas in the Southern Hemisphere where the fallout is appreciably less.* But if the population is unable to maintain its high dietary standards, then food contamination could produce bone levels about five times greater than those calculated above,† with a corresponding increase in cancer incidence (10 per cent incidence of bone cancer, 25 per cent incidence of leukemia).

Additional biological damage would be incurred from yttrium 91, iodine 131, cesium 137, cerium 144, plutonium 239, and others. Zinc 65 is known to be selectively concentrated in fish, and thus, as in the Marshall Islands, would contribute to the body burden of a population that ate a good deal of fish. On the other hand, barium 140 appears to be derived about 25 per cent from milk, 25 per cent from flour, up to 25 per cent from potatoes, and the rest from other food products. Meat from grazing animals, such as beef and lamb, tends to be especially high in cesium 137. Meats of this type probably provide one quarter of the human body burden in America, although most of the radiocesium is derived from milk. The intake of radioiodine by children (mainly from contaminated water and plant products, but perhaps also from fresh milk in nontarget areas), and the biological damage derived therefrom, remains uncertain, but it is possible that the incidence of thyroid

---

* Strontium resembles calcium chemically, and to some extent living organisms confuse these two elements. Animals tend to discriminate against strontium, so that animals eating contaminated plants end up with less strontium in their meat and milk than was in the original plant. Currently about 78 per cent of the calcium contained in human bones in the United States is derived from milk products (16 per cent from plant products and 6 per cent from meat). In contrast, milk products provide only 38 per cent of the strontium 90 (60 per cent from plant products and 2 per cent from meat).

† This was observed in bone samples taken in Recife, Brazil, where the diet is low in meat and milk.

cancers might be severalfold the incidence of bone cancer and leukemia.*

Contaminated farm land need not necessarily remain useless if the social and economic disruption has not been too extensive. The Agricultural Research Service suggests the following measures to restore or rehabilitate the land. Lime can be applied, to increase the calcium-to-strontium ratio in the soil, or fertilizer can be added, which will provide increased potassium concentrations and thus reduce the uptake of both calcium and strontium. The land can be used for crops less likely to pose a strontium-90 contamination problem. If only the upper several inches of soil are contaminated, the land may be diverted to deep-rooted plants—for example, from grass to alfalfa—because such plants obtain their nutrients primarily from below the contaminated layer. In soils not too heavily contaminated, food plants, such as potatoes, could be raised, which contain only about 10 milligrams of calcium per 100 calories, whereas leafy vegetables may contain ten to one hundred times as much. In other words, it might be possible to grow those plants used for human consumption which tend to accumulate the least amount of calcium, and therefore strontium, per unit weight eaten. Another diversion is to human foods that are first processed and hence partially purified, such as sugar, oil crops, and, to some extent, grain (white bread has a much lower strontium-90 content than whole-wheat bread).

Lands too heavily contaminated for the production of food directly consumed by humans might still be useful for raising animals. Since the strontium-to-calcium ratio is lower in meat than in milk, and since meat contains less calcium, and therefore less strontium, a farmer might readily divert from dairying to beef production. Finally, the land might be taken out of food production altogether and used instead for crops such as cotton, flax, castor beans, or timber. If the land was covered by sod or a mulch at the time of the fallout, the removal of this ground cover may eliminate over 90 per cent of the contamination. Similarly, scraping the top two inches of soil with a road grader may remove between 60 and 99 per cent of the fallout strontium. Deep plowing to eighteen inches also might reduce the strontium contamination for shallow-

---

* It has been estimated that in children, one microcurie of radioiodine per gram of thyroid (total dose of 5 microcuries) would result in an integrated dose of about 150 roentgens. About 200 roentgens of X rays applied to the necks of one hundred young children may produce thyroid cancer in about three of them.

rooted crops, but only to about one half its original level. In addition to these techniques, other investigators have suggested that controlled burning in heavily contaminated areas might be an economic way of disposing of badly contaminated crops. Apparently, the radionuclides (e.g., strontium 90, cesium 137) liberated to the soil by the fire are nowhere near as available as the nutrient elements (e.g., calcium, potassium) liberated by the ashed crops.

Thus, a modern well-equipped farmer should be able to cope with many of the fallout-contamination problems, provided they are not too severe. However, if the national attack pattern has been too disruptive or the local fallout field has been too intense, then these considerations become academic.

Because the primary requirements for operating a mechanized farm, like its industrial counterpart, the modern factory, are fuel and power, the disruption of transportation and the destruction of power sources might cause agricultural production to slump almost as dramatically as industrial production. It might be argued that a hundred years ago farmers had neither electricity nor tractors but managed to work their land with power from horses and windmills. But today, out of a total national power production of 11,000,000 khp (kilohorse power), work animals provide only 2,790 khp and windmills only 44 khp. It is also possible that most of the work animals will be killed by fallout radiation, thus limiting some farms to manual labor. In addition, certified seeds of disease-resistant strains, fertilizer, machinery, spare parts, and what might be crucial in a post-attack environment, herbicides, pesticides, and insecticides, might be in short supply for years, thereby further reducing productivity.

There are currently in storage extensive inventories of certain foodstuffs. These provisions, although plentiful, are finite; however, they could probably tide over the surviving population, provided that transportation were available to distribute them.

Thus, if existing stockpiles of food could be transported to the survivors and if the social and economic structure of the society remained stable enough for farmers to regain productivity, then famines would not occur. But if the country is not resilient enough to cope with the extensive destruction and concomitant disorganization that might well follow a nuclear attack, then the degenerating economy will have famine as one of its inevitable consequences.

THE DOWNWARD SPIRAL: Social and Economic Consequences

A modern industrial economy consists of a network of interlocking and interdependent activities so delicately balanced that a break-down in one area often causes serious stresses and strains in other parts of the economy. New Yorkers and others will remember a strike by that city's subway motormen in December 1957. Not only were major portions of the subway system thrown out of service, but many other activities were also affected: subway vendors were deprived of a means of livelihood; department-store sales declined sharply as few shoppers appeared; newspapers suffered a financial loss since both sales and advertising declined; gasoline consumption increased as more people took cars and taxis; more policemen were assigned to traffic duty. In other words, the loss of the services of a few hundred people affected the economy of the entire city.

Although there was much individual deprivation and discomfort in the motormen's strike, the industrial complex of the city could absorb this failure since other means of transportation remained intact. However, far more serious situations can arise. For example, power failure affecting a five-square-mile area of Manhattan in June 1961 left people trapped in elevators, food spoiling in re-frigerators, subways stopped during rush hours, traffic lights inoperative, and hospitals dependent on emergency power supplies. Insofar as the failure lasted only four or five hours, the whole experience could be considered more as an adventure than a catastrophe. However, power failure for an indefinite period of time—or simultaneous breakdowns in a number of critical areas—is obviously quite another matter. Indeed, we may expect that if failure were to occur at a sufficient number of critical points, orderly economic activity would disappear completely.

In the view of Harvard professor Wassily Leontief, who developed the "input-output" concept to describe the functions of an industrial complex, industries are appraised in terms of what other industries provide goods and services to the industry in question (input), and in turn to whom the industry furnishes its own output. In the highly integrated American economy, many industries deliver a large part or even all of their output to other industries which further process the product. For example, the nonmetallic-minerals industry mines the sulfur that is converted into sulfuric acid by the chemical industry. Sulfuric acid is then used by the steel industry to finish the steel sheet that is used by the automobile industry in manufacturing trucks, which are then used by a transportation enterprise.*

Professor Seymour Melman of Columbia University, making use of the concepts developed by Leontief and others, has stressed the vulnerability of the American economy (or that of any other industrialized nation) to nuclear attack. For example, the manufacturing plants of the crucial machine-tool industry are concentrated in Ohio, Michigan, Connecticut, and Vermont, the most important concentrations occurring in major metropolitan centers. Accordingly, destruction of production facilities in these centers would have a more extensive effect than may be indicated by the value of the destroyed industrial assets or the value of the curtailed industrial output. Where the outputs of an industry are crucial to the functioning of many other industries (as in the case of machine tools), the derangement caused by the curtailment of production is multiplied, affecting many other industrial sectors and regions as well. In other words, if one third of the nation's economic assets

* For an interesting application of this type of analysis, namely, to determine the potential effect on employment if the military budget of the United States were to be cut by 20 per cent as a result of disarmament, see W. W. Leontief and M. Hoffenberg, "The Economic Effects of Disarmament," *Scientific American,* Vol. 204 (1961), pp. 47-55.

have been destroyed it does not necessarily mean that two thirds of the economy will be able to function.

The destruction of a single city involves the destruction of many different kinds of economic assets. This can best be illustrated by examining in some detail the economic assets of a specific city like New York. New York City has a population of about 8,000,000 people, with another 5,000,000 living nearby and often directly or indirectly dependent on the city. It is the financial capital of the world, the home of the United Nations, the corporate heart of the nation, the center of American culture, the leading wholesale and retail market of the country, and the transportation and communication hub of the Northeast. Although one tends to think of Pittsburgh or Detroit as being the foremost manufacturing centers of the country, the leading city is actually New York. In 1954, New York City contained 38,000 manufacturing establishments providing jobs for almost a million people. About one third involved apparel and related products, 13 per cent metal products and machinery, and 9 per cent food and kindred products. The Metropolitan Area's warehouses provided 13 per cent of the nation's total storage floor space, and the city's merchants handled 18 per cent of the nation's wholesale products. New York's 112 banking firms represented about 20 per cent of the total assets for all active banks in the continental United States, and 34 per cent of the gross receipts reported by the nation's business service establishments (advertising, research and testing, designing, management, consulting, etc.) went to the 11,000 business establishments in New York.

Not only does New York contain a sizable fraction of the physical plant of the nation's economy, but also an even more significant portion of its intellectual and managerial manpower resources. The seventeen-county New York-northeastern New Jersey Metropolitan Area contains 10 per cent of the nation's total labor force, including 12 per cent of its managers, officials and proprietors (except farm), and professional and technical workers. Residing in this area are 15 per cent of all the nation's physicians and surgeons, 16 per cent of its accountants, auditors, architects, chemists, and electrical engineers, and 17 per cent of its chemical engineers. The size of the last three categories is not surprising insofar as over 20 per cent of the nation's research laboratories are in the New York Metropolitan Area. Considering this heavy concentration of physical and intellectual assets, it is not unreasonable to expect that a single, efficient thermonuclear strike against New York City would deprive the United States of from 5 to 10 per cent of its economic capacity. Attacks on other major industrial centers would produce comparable results, which would reverberate throughout the economic system, having repercussions far from the sites of the attacks.

The general effect of nuclear attack upon the socioeconomic life of a nation relates not merely to the destruction of physical facilities, but also to the production of mass casualties. In the case of a nationwide attack on the major metropolitan areas, the destruction of communication and transportation facilities and the killing and wounding of trained personnel would paralyze the country and make it impossible to utilize remaining resources effectively. In the absence of special blast protection, blast-induced deaths alone, resulting from 400 ten-megaton bombs aimed at metropolitan areas, would eliminate about half of the American population. The 1959 Holifield Hearings estimate that a 1,446-megaton attack would kill 31 per cent of the population and leave 12.5 per cent surviving injured.

F. C. Iklé, in his book *The Social Impact of Bomb Destruction,* cites four principal types of manpower loss: direct loss, consisting of workers killed or seriously injured; indirect loss, due to man-hours spent caring for the injured; loss of morale, which would affect the emotions and motivations of the survivors and thus diminish their work output; and disorganization stemming from casualties among essential business leaders or government officials. Leo Hoegh, then Director of the Office of Civil and Defense Mobilization, testified to the Holifield Committee in its 1960 Civil Defense Hearings that the Federal Reserve System was making vigorous efforts to insure continuity of management following attack. Assuming that a reasonable plan of succession could be developed, there would still remain the problem of whether a former subordinate is capable of assuming the responsibilities of a former director, particularly during times of emergency when the entire system might be disrupted.

For immediate post-attack survivors, destruction of the transportation facilities might prove to be the crucial factor in determining the extent of survival and subsequent rate of recovery.

It could interfere with or prevent the evacuation of a population from a high-risk zone, and it could prevent essential supplies from reaching stricken areas.

New York City is the hub of the nation's most elaborate transportation system. The city is served by about 170 steamship lines, 11 railroads (9 of which are trunk lines), 17 domestic and 26 overseas airlines, about 30 suburban and long-distance bus lines, and several thousand trucking companies. Forty per cent of the country's water-borne exports and imports flow through New York Harbor. An attack on this vital transportation center would destroy not only its major facilities—bridges, tunnels, highways, railroad and bus terminals, airports, docks, garages, depots, and warehouses—but also a considerable amount of transportation equipment. For example, one of the country's largest railroad yards, in Sunnyside, Queens, is well within the zone of serious blast damage. Locomotives and freight and passenger cars would be subjected to a pressure of about 30 psi and would be completely destroyed. Rolling stock would also be inoperative at the Mott Haven yards in the Bronx and at most of the very extensive yards along the west bank of the Hudson River in New Jersey. Similarly, all planes at La Guardia and Teterboro airports would be likely to be destroyed, and most planes at Idlewild, Newark, and Floyd Bennett airports would probably be inoperative.

There are roughly 1,500,000 motor vehicles, including trucks and buses, registered in the city itself, and the great majority of these would be incapacitated. Ships docked along the East River in Brooklyn below the Brooklyn Bridge would be exposed to 10 psi pressure, sufficient to cause serious damage. Ships closer to the explosion would sustain higher pressures; those tied up at the West Side piers of midtown Manhattan would be well within the fireball zone. The damaging or actual destruction of bridges along the East and Harlem rivers would block waterways and further interfere with water-borne traffic.

In the United States almost two thirds of the industrial power requirements (a total of about 45,000,000,000 Btu's) is supplied by burning coal or oil. This source of power would be drastically curtailed by the disruption of the transportation system. The remaining industrial power requirements are satisfied by natural gas (32 per cent) and hydroelectric power (4 per cent). An attack aimed at major hydroelectric dams and gas and oil fields, coupled with the destruction of the transportation centers, would result in a virtual shutdown of American industries.

The Strategic Bombing Survey, in discussing the effects of the bombing raids on Germany in World War II, cites several examples of a decline in munitions production or combat effectiveness as a result of disruption of transportation or loss of fuel supplies. The Survey concludes that the "bombing effort expended to achieve reduction in German air power was excessive." It points out that attacks against aircraft factories were a waste of time because of the shortage of gasoline. The Germans had trouble flying the planes they had; therefore the "success of the attack on oil production had rendered superfluous any further attack on aircraft output." Similarly, in 1945, munitions output in Germany declined precipitously. "Munitions plants were experiencing increasing difficulties in obtaining supplies of coal, raw materials, and components. This factor, more than direct damage to the plants themselves, was the main cause for the fall in output." The last official German report on munitions production was made on March 15, 1945; it predicted the collapse of the German economy within four to eight weeks. A little over seven weeks later, on May 7, Germany surrendered.

S. G. Winter, Jr., of the RAND Corporation, presented testimony to the 1961 Civil Defense Hearing of the Holifield Committee in which he stated he felt an attitude of "cautious optimism" seemed justified when considering the problems of economic reorganization and recuperation following nuclear attack. He stressed the tremendous industrial capacity of the American economy and the fact that the existing food stocks would probably support the surviving population for well over two years. The calculations implied that "recuperation in a period on the order of a decade is probably not physically infeasible. . . ." However, these calculations were based on certain assumptions: one was that the national transportation systems would remain intact; another, that this was also true for other "network industries," such as electric utilities and water supply. The critical, initial period was assumed to have been successfully survived by making effective use of inventories of food, medical supplies, and other necessities, and it was also assumed that the attack was not overly large, or conversely, that the population was not so well protected as to result in a much greater survival of people over resources.

Mr. Winter recognized the tenuous nature of the more optimistic conclusions and did consider the possibility of extensive economic disintegration. He acknowledged that if the inventories are depleted before the production of the necessities of life can be restored, then there exists the possibility that the economic system will go into a spiral of cumulative disorganization, a spiral which will come to an end only at a much lower level of economic life and with, in all probability, a much smaller surviving population. . . .

Eventually, some form of social organization would be reestablished, but that organization may be at the level of self-sufficient families, communities, or regions. Starvation, disease, and exposure would take a heavy toll of lives before such an equilibrium could be reached—and when achieved, the United States would have a primitive economy. . . .

If one speculates on how a complete failure in the recovery effort might occur, the picture one develops is of a situation where the effectiveness of the Federal Government and many State governments is greatly diminished, the banking system disrupted, most surviving firms are bankrupt, electric power and water supply systems are severely damaged, and the transportation network broken in many places, and where few survivors have the responsibility, authority, and plans to do anything about it. . . .

[The threat arises] that when people are unable to meet their minimum needs by the usual and socially desirable means of participating in the production process, they are likely to turn to unusual and socially undesirable means, such as foraging, plunder, and sterile trading in household goods.

This sort of disorder did, in fact, appear in Hiroshima after the atomic explosion. Dr. Hachiya noted that two weeks after the surrender

the ruthless and greedy were ruling the city. . . . People with evil faces and foul tongues were wearing the best clothes. . . . The country was in the clutches of the mean and the unintelligent. . . . A scarcity of sentries made looting easy. During the war no one would have thought of stealing, and goods would lie in open fields without even the need for a guard, but now nothing was safe that was not locked up. . . . The city was infested with burglars. . . . I learned people were looting the supply dump at the engineering corps. Vandals even came with carts and hauled away everything they could carry. . . . Hiroshima was becoming a wicked town. Without police I was not surprised, but I was ashamed.

In the ruins of Hiroshima, money was valueless and cigarettes took over as a medium of exchange. These thirty-five *sen* cigarettes will now bring three hundred to five hundred *sen* in Hiroshima.

Despite all this, Hiroshima recovered. Within about ten years the population had increased by one half and was growing at a rate of 25,000 yearly. However, it was no doubt the immediate and massive aid supplied by the American government in its capacity as an occupying force that contributed heavily to the staving-off of disaster in the winter of 1946 and to the rapid reconstruction of Japan as an industrial power.* In a thermonuclear war no such assistance can be expected.

Underlying the problem of recovery, and in many ways impeding it, is the shift in values that often follows a great disaster. Thus, primary-group, or family, activities predominate over secondary-group, or business, activities.† The fact that concern for the family supersedes concern for the job affects both the immediate and prolonged post-attack problems. For example, right after the attack it would certainly be difficult to activate work crews to make repairs. A telephone lineman is not likely to go out to fix disrupted lines until he has assured himself of the safety of his family. He also may be less inclined to incur personal risk than he would under normal circumstances, because not only would he have been sensitized by the traumatic experience of the attack, but also he may feel that his family needs him more than ever during the time of crisis. Other key personnel would experience the same conflict. In attending to their families, organization and community leaders are likely to neglect their leadership roles. This means that at a time when leadership is most needed it is most apt to be lacking.

Delay in socioeconomic repair could perpetuate disorganization and impede recovery in much the same way that delay in mechanical repair might result in permanent damage to equipment. A shop

---

* Between July 1945 and December 1954 the United States provided almost $30,000,000,000 in foreign aid, plus $2,750,000,000 to the International Monetary Fund, and almost $14,000,000,000 in military assistance. Of these sums, $2,250,000,000 went to Japan.

† See the discussion on primary and secondary groups in Chapter 4. See also: Peter G. Nordlie and Robert D. Popper, *Social Phenomena in a Post-Nuclear-Attack Situation* (Arlington, Virginia: Champion Press, 1961); Allen H. Barton, *Social Organization Under Stress: A Sociological Review of Disaster Studies,* National Research Council Publication 1032 (Washington, D.C.: National Academy of Sciences, 1963); P. H. Liederman and J. H. Mendelson, "Some Psychiatric and Social Aspects of the Defense-Shelter Program" (Part IV of series, Medical Consequences of Thermonuclear War), *New England Journal of Medicine,* Vol. 266 (1962), pp. 1126-55, 1174.

foreman might decide that it is much more important for him to forage for food in the countryside than to report for work, even if his plant produces goods essential to societal reconstruction. This points up the fact that under normal circumstances the roles of shop foreman and family head do not conflict. In fact, they reinforce each other: it is his job that makes him the family provider. In turn, his role as head of the family spurs him on to increase his earnings by doing a better job. This normal socioeconomic situation contrasts sharply with post-attack disorganization. There may not be any money to earn, or money may no longer have any value as a medium of exchange, that is, the job would no longer provide the necessities of life. This would force the individual to abandon his job and perhaps barter his possessions or forage for food and other necessities. If this behavior is carried out on a large scale to the exclusion of important and productive social activities, it would eventually destroy the entire society, since a modern industrial society consists of large productive complexes, not self-sufficient family units. Even if families survived, society as it now exists would not.

That society becomes stagnant, and indeed may disintegrate, when it is reduced to the family level is illustrated by the sociologist E. C. Banfield's study of an extremely poor and backward town in southern Italy. In the absence of any organization beyond the immediate family—the only organizations are the church and the state—the inhabitants of this village are unable to act together for the common good. It is not difficult to imagine how the large-scale destruction and disorientation produced by a nuclear attack might lead to a comparable degeneration of American society.

A population of many individuals crushed by capricious economic and social forces beyond their control looks for extreme remedies to rectify extreme conditions. For example, Germany was not only subjected to the economic and social dislocation caused by World War I, but also to a terrible inflation which for many constituted a threat to their existence much more serious than the war. The combination of new social forces and an unstable economy resulted in a kind of mass neurosis. More and more Germans began to believe that the war was lost, not because superior forces overwhelmed Germany, but because the German army was betrayed at home. And the inflation that further robbed many Germans not only of their life savings, but of their dignity as well, was somehow attributed to the Jews.

This was not the first time the Jews, or other minority groups, had been blamed for a calamity. Although persecutions of the Jews had occurred sporadically during the Middle Ages, it was the Black Death of 1348-9 which resulted in a large-scale pogrom. After the terrible earthquake of 1923 which destroyed Tokyo and Yokohama, many hundreds, and possibly more than six thousand, Koreans were murdered by incensed Japanese who believed that the fires had been started by the Koreans as revenge upon their country's conquerors. Similarly, when London was destroyed by fire in 1666, mobs searched out foreigners, particularly Frenchmen and Dutchmen, because of rumors that they were responsible for the fire. Later this same fire, which started accidentally in a bakery, was blamed on the Catholics. Feeling ran so high that anyone who dared to say that the fire was probably accidental was suspected of being part of a conspiracy to destroy London.

These persecutions were all directed at minority groups readily identified by culture, religion, or language. However, during the 1930's many Americans were guilty of exploiting and mistreating thousands of their fellow citizens, a "minority group" of white, Protestant farmers who had been forced off their land by the Depression or by the drought that converted large areas of the prairie states into the famed Dust Bowl. As thousands of refugees headed west in search of employment—in 1937 over 100,000 unemployed people entered California by car—they were shamelessly cheated along the way, kept from employment or relief, and often hounded by the police as vagrants and undesirables.

If socioeconomic forces, or fires, earthquakes, and epidemics can elicit these scapegoat reactions, it is not unreasonable to expect that the widespread disorganization produced by a nuclear attack would lead to similar persecutions. Moreover, the treatment of the unfortunate migrant farmers also illustrates the problem of refugees, which in the case of a nuclear attack might well take on unprecedented proportions.

During the plague that struck London in 1665, surrounding towns padlocked their water wells, shut up their stores, and posted armed guards on the roads from London to keep out the refugees who were fleeing the city. As a result, many Londoners died of thirst, exposure, and starvation. Three centuries later, the mere threat of nuclear war has produced the same kind of thinking in the United States. Civil Defense officials have already prepared evacuation routes, and in Nevada, local officials considered creating a five-thousand-man militia to repulse potential refugees fleeing bombed areas in Southern California. One official was quoted as saying that if Nevada were not subjected to heavy radiation, "a million or more persons might stream into this area from Southern California. . . . They could come in like a swarm of human locusts . . . [and would] pick the valley clean of food, medical supplies and other goods. Our law enforcement agencies are not numerically equipped to handle such an influx of humanity so we have drawn up plans for a militia." Another official advised Las Vegas residents to build bomb shelters in their backyards, and then went on to say, "If the builder takes a shotgun into the shelter with him as I advocate to protect his family, the head of the family must be prepared to repel invaders—even those who come from across the street."

PESTILENCE AND PLAGUE: The Threat of
Epidemics

Post-attack survivors suffering from exposure, malnutrition, injury, and radiation poisoning are an ideal feeding ground for epidemics. Given the possible destruction or pollution of water supplies, the shortages of disinfectants, insecticides, pesticides, and vaccines, the migration of large numbers of people, and the scarcity of food, one can readily envision epidemics of a magnitude not seen on this continent for over a century.

After the atomic bombings of Hiroshima and Nagasaki, the public-health problem was acute—infected wounds further complicated by filth, swarms of disease-carrying insects, lack of medical personnel and supplies—but there were no major outbreaks of epidemic diseases. This was undoubtedly because the surrounding countryside came to the aid of the stricken cities, sending in rescue teams and supplies and evacuating survivors.

However, a thermonuclear attack on the United States might well produce a very different set of circumstances. First of all, the total atomic casualties in Japan represented less than three tenths of 1 per cent of the Japanese population,* as contrasted

* The combined deaths resulting from the Hiroshima and Nagasaki bombings about three months after the attacks amounted to slightly over 100,000; the total casualties involved about 200,000. The combined population of the two cities at the time of the bombing was 429,000. The population of Japan in 1945 was about 72,000,000.

with the Holifield-attack estimates of an anticipated 47,000,000 killed and 18,800,000 injured, out of an assumed United States population of 150,700,000. Furthermore, the Japanese did not have to contend with fallout. In the presence of fallout, it is unlikely that the surrounding countryside would be able to come to the aid of the moribund American cities, and thus the relief operations and general cleaning up witnessed at Hiroshima and Nagasaki would not take place except perhaps in the lightly hit parts of the United States.

In considering post-attack public-health problems it is helpful to consider infectious diseases in terms of the following categories: First, there are the "demic" diseases, which are endemic in human populations and are exemplified by intestinal infections such as typhoid and dysentery, and by respiratory infections such as influenza and tuberculosis. Second, there are the "zootic" diseases, which normally occur only rarely in humans but are common among animals. Such diseases, including tularemia and plague, currently are not a serious problem in the United States because of ecological and sanitary barriers (which break down only under very rare, individual circumstances). Another potential hazard are diseases such as louse-borne typhus and yellow fever, which are not found in the United States at present, but which, having gained a foothold (accidentally or deliberately) following a nuclear attack, could create a most serious public-health problem.

Needless to say there are many other diseases that might take a tremendous toll in human lives if they were to become rampant. Leprosy, malaria, syphilis, diphtheria, and other diseases that do occur in the United States but are kept under control might become serious menaces if ecological barriers or public-health controls were to fail. Many of these proved to be problems in Europe as a consequence of the breakdown of social organization and services in devastated areas during World War II. However, epidemics were sporadic and mostly local; only the incidence of infectious social diseases, such as tuberculosis and venereal diseases, increased everywhere.

On the whole, the epidemic situation during and following World War II was much better than that following World War I. Several factors accounted for this improvement: progress, both in prevention and treatment prior to and during the war; the rapid development of health services between the two wars; and, partially as a by-product of this development, the greatly reduced endemic level of nearly all important epidemic diseases. In addition, the world was spared the influenza pandemic of 1918, "the most catastrophic outbreak of infectious disease of modern times," which killed about 21,000,000 people and probably incapacitated another 500,000,000.

The above factors should also apply to a nuclear-attack situation, but only if destruction is not too extensive, if there is nothing comparable to the influenza pandemic, and if a minimum of public sanitation can be maintained. The greater understanding of the causes and treatment of most of the serious diseases, coupled with the low endemic rate of most of these, should result in a picture not too dissimilar from the one in Europe during the mid-1940's.

However, if there were widespread destruction the whole picture would change dramatically. The Strategic Bombing Survey concluded that had the Germans not been forced to surrender when they did, "disease would have become rampant." Furthermore, some of the very factors that favor a lower epidemic rate if destruction is not too widespread have the reverse effect if the opposite is true. The low endemic level is helpful insofar as it gives a society respite before the epidemic develops into full force. On the other hand, the absence of a specific microbe leads to a reduction in immunity in a population since there has been no challenge presented them by the particular organism and hence no build-up of immune defenses. For example, typhus broke out in Germany during World War II, but it was found primarily among workers imported from Eastern and Central Europe. However, among those Germans who did contract the disease, the mortality rate was about four times as high as it was among foreign laborers (24.5 vs. 6.5 per cent).

Although there was extensive destruction in Germany and other European countries, it seems relatively minor in comparison to a nuclear attack. Furthermore, as in Japan, the intervention of large-scale American aid rapidly helped to restore European sanitation standards to their prewar status.

The circumstances under which typhus, dysentery, tularemia (rabbit fever), and plague have appeared in epidemic form illustrate how, in the twentieth century, serious public-health problems can arise. It must be clearly understood that these examples have been chosen purely for illustration, not for prediction.

Typhus fever is an acute infection characterized by fever and rash and caused by certain species of viruslike bacteria (rickettsiae). At least three forms of the disease are recognized: scrub typhus, transmitted by mites, which has never been found in the United States, but which is widespread throughout the southwestern Pacific area and in southeastern Asia; endemic or murine typhus, a mild, flea-borne form found in the southeastern United States; and epidemic or classic typhus, which is louse-borne and is attended by a high mortality rate.

When there is poverty, famine, and crowding, particularly in communities where the social order has been upset by war, epidemic or louse-borne typhus may become a real menace. It has frequently devastated armies and has wreaked havoc among refugee and other civil populations that are the victims of war. For example, the impact of World War I set off a ground swell of typhus fever, the effects of which outlasted the war itself by some five years. On the other hand, although tens of thousands of cases did occur, the World War II situation was much less serious. This was due mainly to the initial lower endemic level in Europe, the prominent use of DDT, and the greatly strengthened public-health organizations.

A situation where the public-health services did break down and were thus unable to cope with the threat of a major typhus epidemic arose in Naples in 1943. The first cases of typhus reported in Italy since the 1920's occurred in the city of Bari in March, and in Aversa in April 1943, with other scattered cases in several villages in southern Italy. In Naples the first authentic case was reported in July 1943. It is not known how typhus entered Italy, but it is quite likely that it was brought in by refugees entering Italy from the Balkan countries or by Italian prisoners of war returning from Tunisia.

Following the original introduction of typhus into the practically nonimmune population of southern Italy, the incidence of cases rose rapidly. Apparently the disease had been brewing in Naples during the late spring and summer months of 1943. As colder weather approached, more and more cases were reported: in October, 29 cases, in November, 61, between the end of November and December 5, 26 new cases, while the next ten days saw 83 more arise. The addition of 288 new reports by the end of December clearly illustrated the mounting tempo.

The conditions in Naples and, in fact, in all of southern Italy were ripe for the development of a major typhus epidemic. In Naples, estimates of the civilian population varied between 750,000 and 1,000,000 persons. In addition there were hundreds of Allied soldiers, returning Italian civilians, and refugees from other war-torn parts of Italy and from across the Adriatic. Living conditions were congested and unsanitary. Telephone, transportation, water, light, and sewer systems were disrupted. Medical personnel for the most part were in the army. Food was scarce, black-market prices exorbitant; hence, undernourishment was striking. Leadership had changed so fast that most people scarcely knew which way to turn or whom to believe. The bombings and terrorist activities of the Germans and the bombings by Allied Forces kept the cold and hungry people in a constant state of fear and anxiety.

At the first wail of the air-raid alarm, thousands poured from their homes and crowded into the numerous shelters scattered throughout the city. These shelters were primarily large caverns honeycombed in the limestone formations that comprise the hills on which Naples is built. In some of these rooms thousands of people were found living under primitive conditions, many without beds, bedding, or other household effects. In addition to the shelters formed from natural caverns, there were many small shelters of reinforced concrete located along the railroad yards and dock areas. No sanitary facilities were available in most of them and people lived in their own grime and disease. Many homes were nearly as filthy and crowded as the shelters. In some instances, two and three families were living crowded into two rooms in dark, damp buildings. Children were dirty and poorly clothed. With no soap, no fuel, and poor food, there was very little incentive to keep clean, and louse infestation soon became widespread.

The typhus outbreak in southern Italy would probably have developed into an epidemic of disastrous proportions had it not been for the intervention of a well-equipped American army, which supplied the administrative leadership and the technical skill necessary for the rapid mass delousing with DDT dusters. Within a very short time the situation was brought under control. Similarly, in 1945, the final disintegration of Germany brought a serious flare-up of typhus, but it was promptly controlled by the occupational authorities. In both these instances, the environmental conditions were not unlike what we might expect after a nuclear attack.

Another disease associated with poor sanitation is dysentery, the traditional scourge of soldiers. It was by far the commonest cause of disability during the American Civil War. It is common in the tropics and occurs frequently in rural areas of the southern United States, most often in early summer. In 1960, there were approximately 3,400 reported cases of amebic dysentery (amebiasis), and nearly 12,500 cases of bacillary dysentery (shigellosis) in the United States. The mortality rate was about 2.5 per cent of total cases, i.e., about 400 reported deaths.

Actually these figures are somewhat misleading. For example, there is evidence that from 5 to 10 per cent of the population of the United States harbors *Entameba histolytica*, the causative organism of amebic dysentery, though without any symptoms. In many of these cases stress on the individual, such as excessive fatigue or malnutrition, may produce a flare-up of the disease. Since radiation is one of the most effective agents known to reduce resistance to infection, it is probable that among an inadequately-cared-for irradiated population there would be outbreaks of intestinal infections.

Wherever large numbers of people are massed under conditions that hinder the maintenance of proper standards of hygiene, bacillary dysentery becomes an almost constant menace. Armies, refugee camps, orphanages, prisons, and mental hospitals are particularly vulnerable to epidemics of this disease. Among the factors that can bring about these outbreaks is the increased opportunity for the completion of the food-feces-food cycle offered by crowding and by the presence of carriers of mild cases who remain ambulant.

In general, warm weather favors the presence of flies, and because of its habits and body structure, the housefly is peculiarly suited for an important role in the transmission of gastrointestinal diseases such as typhoid and dysentery. Flies feed readily on the filthiest excreta as well as the daintiest food materials, and they pass freely from human excrement or sputum to clean, appetizingly prepared food. Their sticky feet, proboscis, and body are excellent mechanical carriers for bacteria and other disease-causing organisms, and their habit of regurgitating droplets and extruding bits of excrement from their digestive system when feeding add to their efficiency as spreaders of disease.

The prevalence of dysentery has greatly diminished because of improvements in sanitation, particularly through improved methods

of disposal of human feces. When these barriers break down, however, the disease may flare up again, as illustrated by the dysentery
epidemic in Berlin during the summer of 1945. In the month of
June alone, almost 5,800 cases were reported, with 420 deaths.
At this time, too, a typhoid epidemic began, with 111 cases reported in June, 382 cases in July, and more than 1,100 cases during
the first three weeks of August.

Typhus, dysentery, and typhoid are examples of human diseases
that break out when sanitary safeguards become inadequate, often
during times of social stress. However, there are other diseases
which infect animals independently of man, and under normal
circumstances are passed on to human beings only rarely. If as a
result of some calamity the relationship between human beings and
infected animals is changed so as to greatly increase the contact
between the two populations, then these "animal diseases" may
cause serious public-health problems.

It is not difficult to envision those conditions following nuclear
attack that might alter the relationship of man to other species:
thousands of people foraging for food, perhaps water, most likely
fuel, to supplement inadequate rations, a phenomenon characteristic
of many a war-torn region in the past. In addition, war frequently
causes ecological changes that permit some species to proliferate
profusely; the customary profusion of rats in a destroyed city is an
example of this.

An interesting war-caused ecological upset occurred in the
Soviet Union during World War II. In 1941, as a result of wartime
conditions in many areas, most crops were not harvested but were
left in the fields instead. This led to a great multiplication of mice,
which was further encouraged by the cover of weeds that sprang
up over the uncultivated farm land. The increase in the number
of mice (and perhaps other rodents) apparently contributed significantly to outbreaks of tularemia, which plagued both the German
and Russian armies, as well as local civilians. One outbreak near
Rostov-on-Don, affecting 37,000 people, was suspected of having
resulted from the victims' sleeping in barns infested with mice that
had contracted the disease. Another outbreak seems to have begun
when grain-handlers inhaled dust that had been contaminated by
mouse feces.

Tularemia is caused by *Pasteurella tularensis,* a bacterium that
has remarkable infective powers, apparently being capable of

penetrating the human skin. The invading organisms establish themselves, multiply locally, and invade the lymphatics from which they are transported to the regional lymph nodes, which become enlarged. At this point there appear sudden and prostrating constitutional symptoms, including fever. Actually, the disease may invade the body via any of several routes. The disease symptoms are related to the particular site of entry and result in a variety of clinical types.* Even when the disease is not fatal, its course is usually protracted. Convalescence is accompanied by much weakness and generally lasts several months, although it may last as long as a year.

Tularemia is frequently contracted from handling the carcasses of infected birds or animals. Rabbits have been incriminated in most cases of direct contact, but infection may also result from the bite of an infected cat, kitten, dog, hog, lamb, wild boar, or even snapping turtle. The consumption of infected food or water also may cause the disease. In Russia, in 1935, there were forty-three cases among peasants who drank water from a brook thought to have been contaminated by sick water rats. In the United States, sheepherders, butchers, and shearers are in special jeopardy because they are in contact with infected sheep or the wood ticks that are the parasites of these animals.

Among the most effective transmitters of tularemia are horseflies and deerflies. These aggressive bloodsuckers are serious pests of livestock, and on occasion they do attack man. These flies may carry tularemia germs on their beaks, thus transmitting the disease from sick to healthy animals, and sometimes to man. In the summer of 1935, when the Civilian Conservation Corps was preparing a game refuge on salt marshes near Bear Lake, Utah, they found the deerflies particularly annoying. Within two weeks over one sixth of the men had contracted tularemia and the camp had to be closed. It is obvious that with the hundreds of isolated cases of tularemia that occur each year in the United States—in 1960 there were 390 reported cases—there are many potential focuses of infection. This

---

* Clinical types of tularemia include: (1) the ulceroglandular or cutaneous type, in which the original site of infection progresses to an ulcer and is accompanied by an enlargement of the regional lymph nodes—case fatality is moderate; (2) the oculoglandular or ophthalmic type, which begins as conjunctivitis and generally results from the introduction of the agent into the eye by hands soiled with *Pasteurella tularensis*—the case fatality is fairly high; (3) the typhoidal or cryptogenic type, which closely resembles typhoid fever in its symptoms—blood poisoning occurs and the case fatality is very high.

situation would present a serious public-health problem if the normal barriers between man and infested animals were to break down.

Closely related to *Pasteurella tularensis* is the highly pathogenic bacterium *Pasteurella pestis*. This organism produces diseases in many species of mammals, particularly in rodents, and in humans is the cause of both the bubonic plague and the Black Death, the pneumonic variant of the same disease.

Human beings can contract plague in one of two ways: through the bite of an infected arthropod, typically the flea *Xenopsilla cheopis*, or by direct contact and handling of plague-infected animals. *Xenopsilla cheopis* feeds on both rat and man, frequently transmitting the disease whenever contact between an infected rat population and a human population makes such cross-infections possible. The bacteria multiply in the flea, increasing in number over a period of weeks. The flea itself may survive for long periods in bags of grain or other commodities. This means that *Pasteurella pestis* can be transported around the world, either by infected rats or, if climatic conditions are favorable, by infected fleas (which infect rats at the port of destination). Plague did enter the United States through the West Coast ports around the turn of the century and through the Gulf Coast ports of New Orleans in 1914 and Galveston in 1920. Currently, strict quarantine has proved effective in preventing the spread of plague, but whether effective measures can be maintained after a nuclear attack is questionable. Badly needed relief supplies might therefore act as a factor in transmitting the disease.

If a person is infected with plague by the bite of an infected flea, then he would contract the bubonic form of the disease. Once the bacteria have entered the body they multiply rapidly and invade the lymph nodes. These lymph nodes swell, giving rise to the characteristic buboes of this disease. Eventually the entire blood stream may become invaded, and sometimes even the lungs. The pneumonic or Black Death form of the disease is contracted from breathing in the plague bacteria, which then invade the lungs. It is characterized by fever, increasing pulse and respiration, increasing cough, ultimately with blood-colored sputum contaminated by many plague bacteria, pain all over, breathing accompanied by a whistling rattle (sibili and *râles*), restlessness, with some delirium finally leading to unconsciousness. At about this time, the patient's face assumes the typical purple color from which the name "black death" is derived. The disease takes about two days to run its course and mortality is virtually 100 per cent, although if certain antibiotics and sulfa drugs are administered early enough they can drastically reduce the case fatality rate. These drugs must be given early because the drug attacks the bacteria, not the toxin which is produced by the bacteria and which is responsible for the patient's death.

In the United States, there were only two deaths in 1961 attributable to plague. Both cases occurred in New Mexico: one victim was a Boston scientist on a geological survey, the other a sheepherder. This exemplifies the current status of the plague problem in the United States, a problem that has a history dating back to the first human case reported in San Francisco in March of 1900.

It is probable that trade with the Orient resulted in the infection of the rats of San Francisco sometime prior to the turn of the century. By 1910 ground squirrels were known to be plague-infected in the coastal region of California from San Francisco south to San Luis Obispo, indicating an early and rapid establishment of an extensive natural reservoir of the disease. Human epidemics in San Francisco, a smaller outbreak in Seattle, and a single case in Los Angeles accompanied the earlier manifestations of plague in rodents. Subsequently, outbreaks occurred in Oakland and Los Angeles, as well as sporadic cases in other parts of California and in Oregon, Nevada, and Utah.

Plague spread gradually among the wild rodents, without attracting attention until 1934. In 1935, the Public Health Service, through a series of widespread studies, discovered that plague had been progressing steadily into the interior of the continent and was demonstrated in many kinds of wild rodents, primarily ground squirrels, wood rats, and prairie dogs of ten states. It was found in virtually every type of terrain, from seacoast to mountain, from desert to forest, from valley to plateau. This great reservoir of plague infection in the West shows every indication of being permanent. If the infection continues to spread eastward there will be the unpleasant possibility of infection of the urban rodent population (rats and mice) of cities in the central and eastern United States. This means that sylvatic plague (plague of woodland animals) would spread to the rodents that associate with humans. If the density of these rodents is sufficiently great, and the number of fleas per rat is sufficiently high, an epizootic (epidemic among the animal population) is likely to ensue—a circumstance that frequently precedes outbreaks of human bubonic plague.

After a nuclear attack, human plague epidemics might originate in the United States in several ways. Bubonic plague, which arises as a result of more intimate contacts between human beings and rats, could easily develop. This would require not only a breakdown in the barriers between man and rat, but also an epidemic among the rats themselves, since in classical bubonic plague almost all human cases result from exposure to infective rat fleas, rather than from exposure to humans infected with the plague bacilli.

The breakdown in barriers between man and rat is most likely following a nuclear attack, since a city reduced to rubble provides an ideal breeding ground for rodents. Even in nonurban areas not directly affected, standards of rat-proofing are likely to decline in the wake of the collective stress placed on the country by an attack which may have destroyed most of its cities. Of course, it is possible that the existing rodent population surrounding a nuclear-bombed city would be destroyed by fallout, but, on the other hand, the migration from outside the fallout field might replenish this decimated rodent population.

Instructive in assessing the potential problem of plague in a nuclear-destroyed city is the outbreak in San Francisco the year following the earthquake of 1906. The first case of plague was reported on August 14, 1907, and was quickly followed by others. Local and state health authorities immediately made efforts to control the disease, but by September 4 the mayor of San Francisco was forced to send a telegram to the President requesting Federal assistance. Dr. Rupert Blue was dispatched to take charge of plague-suppressive measures:

He found that the disease was widespread, that cases had occurred in all parts of the city, and that the difficulties of the situation were increased by the disorganized and ruined condition of the city consequent to the earthquake and conflagration of April 1906.

San Francisco was undergoing a period of reconstruction. The streets in the burned districts were littered with all kinds of debris, and in certain sections of the city many persons were living under most insanitary conditions. Some districts were very much congested because of the sudden influx of refugees and the lack of legal restrictions regarding the placing of frame cottages and the building of stables. . . . Most of these abodes were without any of the ordinary sanitary conveniences. . . .

In some locations speculators had built large, irregular camps covering an area of one or two blocks. In these, sewer connections and toilet accommodations were often most inadequate. The camps themselves were filthy in the extreme, and in some the conditions were deplorable. Uncovered holes in the earth from which flies rose in clouds served as latrines. Washwater and slops ran under and between the shacks, garbage was promiscuously scattered, and rubbish of all sorts littered the premises. The shacks themselves were nondescript affairs, constructed of scraps of sheet iron and bits of old lumber. Because they were close to the ground they afforded excellent rat harborage.

The majority of the stables in the city were hastily constructed buildings without any sanitary arrangements whatever. Grain was kept on the floor in sacks or in open wooden bins, no care was taken to prevent the entrance of rats and very few stables were provided with suitable manure bins. There were numerous chickenyards throughout the city, and the unconsumed food therein furnished a ready source of food for rats. . . . Stables with wooden floors close to the ground, planked yards, debris in the vacant lots, defective basements, and cellars all afforded a safe shelter for rats. . . . Coincident with this condition, fleas were unusually prevalent.

This was the general picture of the city of San Francisco at the beginning of the second plague epidemic in 1907. These conditions could not start a plague epidemic, but once the seed was planted, it had very fertile soil in which to grow.

Vigorous public-health efforts, consisting principally of an effective antirat campaign, brought the situation under control, but not before one hundred and sixty-seven cases (almost all bubonic), with eighty-nine deaths, had occurred.

The second, and more likely, way in which human plague could start is illustrated by an outbreak of pneumonic plague in Oakland, California, in 1919. The initial case was a man who became ill a few days after shooting and dressing ground squirrels for food. Fourteen people contracted the disease, thirteen of whom died. This particular outbreak is not too different in principle from the sequence of events that led to the first Manchurian outbreak of 1910-11. The epidemic began with a few isolated cases among fur trappers, and its spread was hastened by the hot, humid, and crowded underground inns of the town of Manchouli, where the trappers lodged. As the first few cases of the fatal coughing and blood-spitting disease began to multiply, the inhabitants of Manchouli became frightened, and, beginning in September 1910, as many as could do so escaped to the east and south on the Chinese Eastern Railway. At several points along the route some of the sick and feverish left the train, thus spreading plague among the healthy and unsuspecting. The disease spread quickly, and by the time it was finally brought under control, at least 60,000 people had succumbed to the Black Death.

Two features of this epidemic are particularly noteworthy: the initial human involvement resulted from the handling of infected animal carcasses; and once this human infection had occurred, the further spread of the disease involved only human contacts and did not require the presence of athropod vectors. Furthermore, this epidemic took place in the absence of a great natural or military disaster.

Current ecological and sanitary standards in the United States are sufficient to keep plague and most other infectious diseases in check. However, if as a result of nuclear war and its aftermath, we are once again forced into nature, or are unable to maintain those barriers against our natural enemies which we have so carefully built up over the years, then the rodents, the flies, the mosquitoes, the fleas, and all the other noxious carriers of disease will once again become a prominent part of our environment.

Part III THE LEGACY

10

STERILITY AND SENESCENCE: Somatic Effects

Exposure to sublethal doses of radiation is known to produce a number of delayed effects. A thermonuclear attack, which would expose many people to radiation, is likely to cause an increased incidence of degenerative diseases and various forms of cancer. We may also expect an acceleration of aging processes and a consequent shortening of life span, loss of visual acuity through cataracts and other disorders, and an increased incidence of sterility or reduced fertility. Radiation may also adversely affect the normal course of human development and may produce congenital malformations.*

A sufficient dose of localized radiation to almost any part of the

* What knowledge exists in these areas has been subjected to exhaustive surveys by many authors and panels, including the following: T. Stonier, R. E. Beardsley, J. Lipetz, and S. Socolar, *Radiation, Its Biological Effects, and the Fallout Problem* (New York: Scientists' Committee for Radiation Information, 1960); *The Biological Effects of Atomic Radiation: A Report to the Public* (Washington, D.C.: National Research Council of the National Academy of Sciences, 1956); *The Biological Effects of Atomic Radiation: Summary Reports* (Washington, D.C.: National Research Council of the National Academy of Sciences, 1960); Committee on Pathologic Effects of Atomic Radiation, *Long-Term Effects of Ionizing Radiation from External Sources,* National Research Council Publication 849 (Washington, D.C.: National Academy of Sciences, 1961); *Report of the United Nations Scientific Committee on the Effects of Atomic Radiation* (New York: United Nations, 1962); Robert E. Beardsley, "Radiation and Control," in *The Natural Philosopher,* Vol. 1 (New York: Blaisdell Publishing Co., 1963).

body may produce leukemia and other forms of cancer—the larger the dose, the greater the probability that cancer will develop. Studies on the incidence of leukemia in various irradiated human populations have been made on radiologists, patients subjected to X rays (for diagnostic or therapeutic purposes), and the bombed Japanese populations. At Hiroshima it was found that at distances where the dosage was above 75 roentgens there appeared to be a direct 1 to 1 correlation between the incidence of leukemia and the size of the dose. Other studies have shown that if 1,000,000 children were each to be irradiated with 1 roentgen, then at least one, and perhaps five, cases of leukemia would likely result. But if 1,000,000 children were each exposed to 100 roentgens (or if 100,000,000 children were each exposed to 1 roentgen), then between one hundred and five hundred cases would probably arise. In children irradiated prenatally, the probability is two to ten times as great: even in peacetime, prenatal X-ray exposure increases the probability of contracting leukemia by about 40 per cent. Thus, if a population were to receive 300 roentgens in the first week after exposure to fallout radiation, followed by an additional 100 roentgens during the first year, one might expect a leukemia incidence of up to 2,000 cases per million in the first year. In Hiroshima the peak incidence occurred five to seven years after the bombing. The incidence of cancer of the lung, stomach, breast, ovary, and uterine cervix also increased among the surviving Hiroshima victims.

According to the first report of the research committee on tumor statistics of the Hiroshima Medical Association, the dose that brings about a doubling of the incidence of all types of cancer appears to be less than 464 roentgens.* Moreover, the increase in incidence showed up in all age groups, which implies that radiation does not merely cause cancer to appear earlier, but truly increases its incidence. The apparent effect of radiation differs by

* The survivors showing a doubling in the rate of cancer incidence were at approximately 1,300 meters (.815 miles) from ground zero at the time of the explosion. At this distance they would have received a dose of about 460 roentgens had they been in the open. However, had they been in the open, they would also have been exposed to 6 psi blast pressure (enough to demolish a brick house), and more than 22 cal/sq cm (sufficient to cause third-degree burns and to ignite clothing). This implies that anyone surviving long enough to develop radiation-induced cancer must have had substantial protection against blast and heat. Such protection is very likely to be associated with considerable shielding. Therefore, it is probable that the radiation dose actually experienced by the 1,300-meter survivors was very much less than the approximately 460 roentgens implied by the air dose. Hence, the doubling dose for cancer induction is well below 460 roentgens.

site and type of malignancy. This may be because specific organs or tissues differ in their radiation sensitivity, or because some body areas develop tumors more rapidly following exposures, whereas others do so only after a prolonged time interval. Perhaps most interesting is that the incidence of all forms of cancer, including leukemia, increases with the size of the dose, with apparently slight but real increases occurring at very small doses, suggesting that either there is no threshold for radiation-induced malignancies, or that such a threshold involves very small doses.*

Among the primary effects of radiation are changes in the blood system. Many of the delayed effects in other organs seem to come from the metabolic and nutritional disturbances associated with an impaired blood supply to these organs. These disturbances lead to a reduction of function and of reparative capacities, and to an increased susceptibility to injury, infection, and disease in general.

Studies of the Marshall Islanders accidentally exposed to fallout after the BRAVO shot in 1954 showed that certain blood elements were still at slightly lower levels seven years after the exposure to fallout, suggesting a persistent irradiation effect on blood-forming function. These effects appeared to be transmitted to the first-generation male offspring: sons of exposed parents had somewhat lower levels of certain types of blood cells (neutrophils, lymphocytes, and platelets) than children of unexposed parents.

Scientists experimenting on rats and mice have found that hardening of the kidneys (nephrosclerosis) with high blood pressure (renal hypertension) and associated generalized hardening of the arteries (arteriosclerosis) are all late effects of total-body irradiation. These disorders may in turn lead to kidney or heart failure and cerebral hemorrhage.

Substantial doses of radiation to mammalian tissues reduce their regenerative capacity, usually to a degree proportionate to the size of the dose. A small dose of 1 roentgen, when applied to about 2,000 mammalian cells, is likely to cause a chromosome break in

---

* Those who support the hypothesis that the threshold for cancer induction either does not exist, or if it exists, is very small (i.e., doses close to those already encountered in nature), point to the fact that "in the only instance in which it has been possible to obtain unequivocal experimental data, the induction of phage growth in lysogenic bacteria, no threshold was found; one ion pair per cell was effective." On the other hand, see Austin Brues, "Critique of the Linear Theory of Carcinogenesis," *Science*, Vol. 128 (1958), pp. 693-9, for a critique of the no-threshold concept of radiation carcinogenesis.

about seven cells. One hundred roentgens produce on the average of one hit per cell, so that the cell is no longer capable of participating in tissue regeneration. (Some cells will receive more than one hit, other cells will receive no overtly damaging hit.) A dose of 500 roentgens is sufficient to destroy the reproductive capacity of 99 per cent of the cell population. The damage to a cell's reproductive capacity first becomes manifest in the cells of the rapidly reproducing tissues, for example, the blood-forming tissues and the epithelium lining the intestines. On the other hand, cells that do not multiply, such as those of mature nervous tissue, do not show evidence of damage, except following high doses.

When an individual is exposed to a substantial dose of radiation, either to his entire body or to a particular area, he can expect that his life span will be shortened. Life expectancy can be reduced when, for example, radiation damages specific tissue, as in the case of dermatitis followed by skin cancer; or when it produces a disease such as leukemia. Generalized changes in the body as a result of radiation-lowered resistance, damage to vasculoconnective tissue, degeneration of certain organs—all can contribute significantly to a shortened life span.

A person may seemingly "recover" from the effects of radiation exposure, but his body is nevertheless left in a somewhat weakened condition. Although this irreparable damage may not be apparent, it is equivalent to premature aging in an actuarial sense, in that it ultimately deprives the individual of part of his expected life span. Whether or not it is the same as the cumulative injury of natural aging is not yet clear. In rodents, dogs, and swine irreparable injury can be measured: even after an interval of presumed complete repair, the lethal dose to 50 per cent of the population (LD50) of a previously irradiated animal population proved to be lower than that of a population never previously exposed.

In general, irradiation increases the incidence and/or the severity of clinically recognized diseases. In other words, diseases may be *induced* as a direct result of irradiation or they may be *advanced* by irradiation, that is, they may appear earlier than they would among nonirradiated subjects. In many experiments, both mechanisms may seem to operate together, with induction of disease being relatively more important in cases of intensive localized irradiation, and advancement of disease relatively more important in whole-body irradiation.

Most of the research in radiation-induced life shortening has been conducted with rodents and lower forms, and there are as yet no data for man that provide a satisfactory basis for quantitative estimation of the over-all life-span effects of radiation. However, humans harboring chronic or latent infectious diseases, or debilitating afflictions of any kind, may suffer an increased risk from certain diseases following radiation. Radiation resistance is apparently correlated with general vigor, for in the laboratory the most radiation-resistant strains tend to be longer-lived and less susceptible to spontaneous infectious diseases.

A higher death rate, proportional to the degree of exposure, was observed in the exposed Japanese population. It has been estimated that for each additional roentgen of exposure, beyond a certain level, the life span of the individual is shortened by five to ten days. Thus, a population exposed to 300 roentgens whole-body radiation within the first week after attack, and an additional 100 roentgens during the first year, may have a life-span reduction of eleven years (400 x 10 days = 4,000 days.)

When the optic lens of the human eye is exposed to high doses of ionizing radiation, cataracts are likely to develop. Radiation cataracts seem to result from damage to the anterior epithelium, which supplies the cells that differentiate into the fibers of the lens. Young animals exposed during prenatal or early postnatal periods show markedly greater lenticular radiation sensitivity than do older animals. Although there is less information on human beings, the lenses of children under one year of age seem more sensitive to radiation than those of older children and adults.

Studies made of Nagasaki survivors showed that of 425 who were between a quarter of a mile and a mile from ground zero, 47 per cent had lens changes. Although the damage in the vast majority of cases was so insignificant that it was invisible with the ophthalmoscope, statistically significant lens changes were present in survivors with no other known early or late evidences of radiation injury. Of the approximately 8,000 exposed survivors of Hiroshima and Nagasaki examined up to 1956 (eleven years after the atomic-bomb explosions), ten cases of severe cataract had been found, although the relationship between these cases and radiation alone is not clear. Children who were seven to ten years old at the time of the bombing (sixteen to nineteen years old when they were examined) were found to have significant loss of visual acuity.

Because the gonads (reproductive organs) are among the most radiation-sensitive organs of the mammalian body, there is a great danger of reduced fertility and sterility from radiation exposure. Even relatively small doses, 30 roentgens or less, produce microscopically detectable temporary changes in these tissues.

In the dog, the animal most similar to humans in radiation sensitivity, protracted irradiation results in a gradual reduction in number, motility, and viability of sperm. This is one of the most sensitive indicators of chronic damage so far observed, being measurable in dogs receiving only 3 roentgens per week; 80 per cent of dogs receiving this dose were sterile at the end of a year, the remaining 20 per cent showed a reduced sperm count, and at the end of two years, by which time 312 roentgens had been given, substantial degeneration of the reproductive tissue (atrophy of the germinal epithelium) was observable. The same 312 roentgens given as a single total-body dose caused only partial and temporary reduction of sperm formation, with recovery to normal levels occurring within one year after irradiation. The 312-roentgen dose given as 6 roentgens a week for one year resulted in reduced sperm count (aspermia), and a slightly higher dose of 375 roentgens given as 15 roentgens a week for about half a year resulted in complete aspermia which was still in effect one year after irradiation.

There is a case of two reactor operators who were accidentally irradiated at the Argonne National Laboratory, one receiving a dose of 12 roentgens, the second approximately 190 roentgens. The sperm count of the first operator dropped from 500,000,000 per milliliter to 1,000,000 in about seven months, and he recovered about fourteen months later.* The sperm count of the second operator dropped from 500,000,000 per milliliter to a level of essentially zero in about ten months. It required another ten months for the count to return to normal. Thus, a male population exposed to a moderately high radiation dose followed by a continuous low dose over a period of several months is likely to exhibit sterility and reduced fertility for many years.

In females, local irradiation of the ovaries can cause profound degeneration of the organ with temporary or permanent sterility, depending upon the dose. Total-body irradiation appears to pro-

* While this would probably not make the individual sterile, it would probably drastically reduce the reproductive capability because there is a correlation between sperm count and semen volume, and the ability to effect conception.

duce even greater effects on the ovaries and on fertility in female animals than local irradiation of the ovaries with equivalent doses. This may be due to greater endocrine hormone disturbances produced by the former.

Because the germinal cells of prepubertal animals, and those embryonic cells destined to form the germinal cells in fetuses, are considerably more radiation sensitive than the germinal elements of sexually mature animals, irradiation of the young and the unborn would cause even more profound depression of reproductive capacity than it would in adults.

Mammalian embryos exposed to as little as 25 roentgens of X rays will suffer far more dramatic and intensive damage than would similarly exposed adults. For example, in rats the embryonic cells of the differentiating nervous system are 2,500 or more times as sensitive as the nerve cells of the adult rat into which they develop. These primitive differentiating cells of the nervous system are probably the most radiation-sensitive cells of the mammalian organism: substantial numbers of them become visibly killed in less than four hours after as little as 40 roentgens are given to the whole body of the mother or the newborn.

In Hiroshima, subnormal head size (microcephaly) was noted in the offspring of women who were pregnant at the time of the bombing. Almost all cases occurred in children who were irradiated within four months after conception. About half of the thirty-one children studied had normal intelligence, the other half were mentally defective. The defects were clearly related to radiation dose: of the fifteen defectives, the maternal history in eleven cases revealed major radiation symptoms after the bombing.

In addition to neurological defects in the fetuses of the bombed Japanese population, total elimination of the fetus also occurred, but because mechanical injury and shock might have been responsible in many cases, it is not certain how much of this was caused by exposure to radiation. Of 177 pregnant Nagasaki survivors, 45 had abnormal terminations (33 miscarriages, 12 premature births); 10 of these women with abnormal terminations died, 8 of them within a week after the bombing. Of the 12 premature infants, 4 were stillborn and 3 died soon after birth. All 19 pregnant survivors who were within 1.18 miles of ground zero had their pregnancies terminate abnormally. Of the women who were somewhat farther away at the time of the explosion (1.18 to

1.8 miles from ground zero), 15 out of 20 terminated abnormally. Beyond 1.8 miles, only 11 out of the 138 exposed pregnant women subsequently experienced abnormal terminations.

Among the exposed Marshall Islanders there appeared to be an increased number of miscarriages and stillbirths for several years after the accident, although this trend seemed to have ceased by five years later. Again it is not ascertainable whether or not this increase was caused primarily by radiation, and if so whether it reflected genetic or physiological damage.

Studies on Japanese children exposed to the atomic bomb in 1945 indicate only a very slight but statistically significant retardation of growth and maturation. However, the influence of other nonradiation factors has not yet been adequately evaluated. Extensive measurements on 4,800 children six, seven, and eight years after exposure in Hiroshima revealed generally that growth was retarded and maturation delayed. In another study of several hundred children in Hiroshima and Nagasaki, made two, four, and five years after irradiation, physical growth and development were reported to be adversely affected, and the resulting retardation of height, weight, and skeletal development was still evident at the end of 1950. But investigators believed that malnutrition and other factors besides radiation may have added to these effects.

Among the Marshall Islanders, retardation was observed not only in exposed children and in children exposed *in utero,* but also in children of exposed parents conceived several years after the fallout accident: the male offspring of the exposed parents were smaller in stature at all ages than those of unexposed parents. This phenomenon has not been explained. One could consider two possibilities: that it has a genetic basis, indicating genetic damage to either the fathers or mothers; or that the mothers alone were responsible, having been so injured by their exposure to radiation that they were no longer capable of producing completely normal offspring.

Boys in the Marshall Islands who were less than twelve years of age when they were exposed to radiation revealed a distinct tendency to be shorter than unexposed males. This reduction in size was prominent in boys under six years of age, and most marked in those exposed at twelve to eighteen months. Although this trend was not observed among the exposed girls, X-ray examinations of the left hand and wrist showed trends suggestive of inferior skeletal maturation in both male and female children. The growth retardation of some of the boys is quite startling: two showed retardation amounting to one and a half to two years, and two others, who were eight and a half years old in 1961, were so retarded that one had a skeletal age of only three years, and the other of three and a half years. It would be helpful if it could be ascertained just how much radiation these children were exposed to at the time of the accident.*

On the basis of the foregoing observations, it is reasonable to expect that a population irradiated enough to kill a few per cent of its members would then have to face serious long-term problems. Such a population, which might have been exposed to 300 roentgens during the first two or three weeks after a nuclear attack, and an additional 100 roentgens during the remainder of the year, would be left in such a weakened condition that it would be unable to cope with the economic and social disorganization of the post-attack environment.

The life expectancy of these people would be cut by about a decade. This would be due partly to a doubling of the incidence of cancerous diseases—leukemia alone would kill two people each year out of a population of one thousand—but mostly to the earlier and more frequent appearance of a variety of degenerative diseases, including heart and kidney failure.

Accompanying the decrease in life span would be reduced vigor and ability to resist infectious diseases, along with drastically curtailed reproductive power. Reduced fertility, and perhaps complete sterility, would be widespread, particularly among those who were young at the time of the attack.

The exposed children would be most profoundly affected by irradiation, in that they would suffer the same somatic disturbances as would adults, but to a greater degree. In particular, the boys who survived would be severely retarded in growth.

Thus, those nuclear-attack survivors who were not able to avoid extensive radiation † would live shorter, less vigorous lives, suc-

---

* The population that received the largest fallout exposure was subjected to an estimated dose of 175 roentgens of whole-body gamma radiation. In addition, the skin was sufficiently contaminated with fallout particles so as to receive beta burns. These burns are caused by the weakly penetrating beta radiation, which destroys the skin and other superficial tissue and forms ulcerating sores.

† The reader is reminded that in a moderately heavy fallout field the outside dose to an unshielded person between the end of two weeks and two months following a nuclear explosion would still accumulate to a total dose of 670 roentgens.

cumb more readily to infectious and degenerative diseases, would have great difficulty in conceiving a new generation, and might also not be able to rear its existing young into viable adulthood. If such a population were forced to face a post-attack environment, with its limited resources, the demise of a large part of the population, if not the entire population, would be virtually assured.

ECOLOGICAL UPSETS: Plants, Insects, and Animals

Until fairly recently, public discussions dealing with fallout were concerned almost solely with the potential effects on man. This emphasis is not only egocentric, it is naïve. For if fallout is capable of killing human beings, it is also capable of killing other creatures, and it is well known that even small changes in nature can lead to a concatenation of events which may ultimately profoundly alter the relationship between man and his environment.

It is difficult to predict the biological upsets that would result if large quantities of radioactive material were to be deposited over the countryside. For example, very small amounts of radioactive phosphorus were released into the Columbia River (which contains little phosphorus) by the Hanford Plant of the United States Atomic Energy Commission. The radiophosphorus entered the food chain and became concentrated along each step so that young swallows in the area were found to have accumulated the radiophosphorus by a factor of 500,000, while some duck and geese eggs were found to contain well over a millionfold the concentration found in the river water.* In spite of the large concentration factors, the ability of the eggs to hatch was not

* The algae in the Columbia River accumulated the radiophosphorus one thousandfold, adult geese and ducks concentrated it 7,500 times over the level found in the water, and adult swallows 75,000 times.

appreciably affected, probably because the initial levels of radio-phosphorus in the river were extremely low. But if higher (but not obviously dangerous) levels of radioactive phosphorus had been discharged into the river, they might have eliminated part of the local bird population, a result that could not have been antici-pated a priori.

The problem of predicting the consequences of heavily con-taminating large tracts of land with fallout stems from a variety of uncertainties. Not only do various organisms accumulate fallout products at different rates, but the same amounts of radioactivity do not result in equivalent amounts of biological damage in dissim-ilar organisms. Furthermore, the mechanism of biological damage varies from one radioisotope to the next. For example, cesium 137 emits gamma rays and is not incorporated, as far as is known, into molecules of great biological significance. This isotope probably exerts its effect inside the body in the same manner as it does when it irradiates the organism from some external source. In contrast, radiophosphorus may enter molecules of great biological signifi-cance, such as nucleic acids, probably disrupting these molecules upon disintegration and thereby causing damage in addition to that induced by radiation.

Most of the damage to mammals who have ingested appreciable amounts of fallout is likely to result from strontium 90. Studies of cotton rats at the White Oak Lake bed, in Oak Ridge, Tennessee, indicated that strontium 90 accounted for over 80 per cent of the radiation dose delivered by the internally deposited radioisotopes. However, what is more important in assessing post-attack ecological upsets is the fact that the cotton rats received only about 10 to 15 per cent of the total dose from ingested radioisotopes: 85 to 90 per cent of the total radiation dose originated from the fallout-contaminated environment in which the rats lived. Therefore it is the external radiation from fallout that is most likely to produce profound upsets.

From an ecological point of view, radiation may be considered merely another form of environmental stress, like excessive wind, cold, or drought. As with other stresses, species vary tremendously in their ability to withstand radiation. For various populations of specific organisms, survival in a fallout field would depend upon the radiosensitivity of the individual members, the amount of radiation that the individuals were actually exposed to, and the reproductive potential of the population. The exposure, of course, could vary even among members of the same species: insect grubs feeding a few inches below ground would get a very much smaller dose than the adults flying around in the fallout field. The greater the reproductive capacity of a population, the better chance it would have of surviving: if only one pair of creatures out of a thousand survived, microorganisms could reconstitute the entire population in a matter of hours, insects in weeks, mammals in years.

In respect to the first variable, the radiosensitivity of various species, it has been found that mammals are most sensitive, almost all being destroyed by a dose of about 1,000 roentgens. Other vertebrates are somewhat less sensitive. Insects are very much more resistant: many are still able to reproduce at doses above 5,000 roentgens, which is ten times more than is needed to kill many mammals. Although many insect eggs are destroyed at doses well below those which kill mammals, adult insects can absorb doses higher than 100,000 roentgens without apparent ill effects. Certain other arthropods, such as mites, as well as certain other invertebrates, such as parasitic nematode worms, are still more resistant than insects. Plants vary in their sensitivity all the way from pine trees and other conifers, which are about as sensitive as mammals, to mustard seeds, which can absorb 92,000 roentgens and still produce viable plants. In general, however, plants tend to suffer appreciably from doses of about 5,000 roentgens.

Thus, we can conclude that radiation would tend to stress, if not actually eliminate, the vertebrate and certain plant populations, while other plant populations and most invertebrate populations, including insects, would hardly be touched. In addition, as we shall see, the indirect effects may prove to be even more serious. Sick and dying plants favor the build-up of populations of plant-eating insects (bark beetles, grasshoppers, etc.). Radiation-damaged plants would therefore present the herbivorous insects with a "preferred" food supply, which would tend to produce insect population explosions. This potentially calamitous situation would be greatly aggravated by the extensive destruction of the birds and mammals feeding on the insects. The result: insect plagues.

Associated with the spread of insects would be the spread of certain insect-borne diseases. Furthermore, large tracts of killed trees would pose serious fire problems. Thus, the plants in and near fallout fields would be subjected to a multiple assault of radiation, insects, disease, and fire. In some areas the plant cover could be damaged, possibly even eliminated, setting the stage for serious erosion problems.

There have been very few actual experiences with the effects of large amounts of fallout in nature. Studies of natural populations of fruit flies were made on Rongelap Atoll, in the Marshall Islands, and it was found that these insects readily survived the heavy fallout to which the islands were accidentally exposed as a result of the March 1954 BRAVO shot on Bikini. Although genetic damage was evident the fly population recovered rapidly. On Rongelap the fruit-fly population had a lowered rate of egg development in August 1955 (about a year and a half after the BRAVO shot), but by August 1956 this effect was no longer apparent. On Bikini itself, on the other hand, the fruit-fly population sampled at that time still showed a lowered rate of egg development, although it did not seem to be a serious handicap to the over-all population.

In nature, the abundance of eggs laid results in crowded conditions, which normally increase the death rate. If a sizable number of the eggs fail to hatch, the surviving larvae have more food available and thus have a better chance of reaching adulthood. It is not surprising, therefore, that scientific investigators reported no difficulty in collecting fruit flies on the fallout-exposed islands except where fly populations appeared to be reduced because of lack of food. In fact, the Marshall Islands surveys indicated that shortages of food, rather than the reduced reproductive capacity, acted as the limiting factor in re-establishing a fruit-fly population following exposure to fallout.

The plants fared far worse. Of a total of fifteen flora species on Gegen Islet, a small island at the northern edge of Rongelap Atoll, thirteen species showed conspicuous injury or death. This islet received a dose estimated at 3,000 roentgens. Five years later, "the most striking feature . . . from the air was the generally gray color of much of the vegetation, in contrast to its normal green color." *

* On Kabelle Islet, also a part of Rongelap Atoll but somewhat farther downwind and to one side of the fallout field, three species showed damage, the mangroves having been completely killed off. On Eniwetok Islet (Rongerik Atoll), which received about one third the dose to which Gegen Islet was subjected, the fallout affected only two species. However, these were sufficiently prominent so that the loss of leaves and dieback of twigs caused the vegetation to be a general gray color. This islet was devoid of fruit flies in 1956.

The injured plants had a variety of pathological conditions: some showed curious mistletoelike or witches-broomlike leafy branches of a dark green color, most showed a loss of leaves and dying back of twigs, while others showed only a yellowing and shriveling of leaves. A small grove of coconut trees near the center of Naen Islet (Rongelap Atoll), also heavily contaminated, contained four or five dead trees decapitated at heights of five to twelve feet above the ground (with no evidence of machete marks). Several trees had dry and shriveled fronds and about six showed deformed bulges. Two double-headed coconut trees were also seen, one of which appeared to be dead.

It is not certain whether all this destruction is directly attributable to the exposure of the plants to fallout radiation. Some of the detrimental effects may have been caused indirectly—the irradiated plants might have been less resistant to drought or to parasites, and therefore succumbed to these additional stresses. Hence, these effects should be considered as due to radiation, albeit delayed.

The vertebrate population on Rongelap Atoll examined for radiation effects included eight swine, one cat, four ducks, forty-one chickens, and nine baby chicks. These animals had received relatively small doses of between 280 and 360 roentgens, depending on the date of removal from the island, i.e., doses well below the LD_{50}. Although malnourished, they showed no other evidence of disease. Autopsy of two chickens that had died during transit revealed no pathological findings that could be associated with radiation. It is interesting to note, however, that all nine baby chicks died spontaneously. The human component of the vertebrate population was subjected to only about 175 roentgens prior to evacuation. Since the effects on adults were minor, while the effects on young children were pronounced, one cannot help but wonder whether the death of the chicks did not also reflect somatic radiation damage.

The observations of the ecological effects of fallout in the Marshall Islands represent only a very limited type of experience, and thus it is difficult to extrapolate from this data to potential events in the United States. With the exception of a few areas, such as the Florida Keys, the flora and fauna of the coral atolls are very different from those in most parts of America. The environment of a coral island is fairly rigorous. The plants must tolerate high salt concentrations and desiccating winds. In addition, the isolation of the Marshall Islands is atypical of conditions on the North American subcontinent. Migration of various creatures into the fallout-damaged zone would tend to ameliorate the adverse effects stemming from local fallout radiation.

Migration can be extremely important in maintaining balanced relationships in nature. Any suitable ecological niche that can support life tends to become filled rapidly with migratory biotypes. This is true not only of animals that can migrate, but also of plants that have reproductive dispersal devices, such as windblown seeds. It should be emphasized, however, that in order to be filled such niches must be accessible to the migrants, and that currently there exists a large reservoir of organisms that are ready to repopulate any niche that becomes temporarily vacant.

If migration into an area by birds and seeds, following serious damage by fallout, is likely to have an ameliorating effect, the reverse may also be true. Insect populations building up in areas subjected to fallout may migrate out to devastate the surrounding countryside. This happened in Oregon after the great Tillamook forest fire of 1933. Douglas-fir beetles bred in the fire-damaged trees, and by 1935 they had developed such large numbers that swarms migrated out of the burned area to attack green timber. In so doing, the beetles destroyed an additional 300,000,000 board feet of valuable timber.

Another incident, involving the vast and majestic Engelmann spruce forests of western Colorado, which were destroyed by bark beetles in the 1940's, provides the best example of what could happen if large tracts of forest were irradiated. In June 1939, a severe windstorm swept across the state and knocked down many of the shallow-rooted spruces. Many of these wind-thrown trees remained alive for years, gaining nourishment from the roots on the down side, and thus they became a fertile breeding place for the Engelmann spruce bark beetles. By 1942, the sick trees had been consumed and the beetles had built up tremendous populations. The beetles then began invading the standing spruces, and by 1943, when the infestation was first discovered, the number of infested trees was so great that it was no longer possible to control the insects with fire or insecticides. By 1948, much of the area that had been covered by the stately green spruces was now a ghost forest.

During the beetles' flight period of 1949, the air was so full of beetles that the ones that happened to fall into a small lake in the infested area and were washed ashore (although only a minor fraction of the total flight) were so numerous that they formed a drift of dead beetles a foot deep, six feet wide, and two miles long. Those flying southeast over eighteen miles of open country settled on a plateau of previously uninfested forest and killed 400,000 trees in one mass attack.

Thus, we have tragic evidence of how fast and silently a tiny insect can do its damage when a combination of favorable factors brings about a population explosion. In six years alone, sixteen times more timber was destroyed than was killed by fire over a thirty-year period in the Rocky Mountain region. Parts of the nation's most beautiful national forests were damaged for a generation.

Just as forest fires and wind damage may bring about conditions favorable to a beetle population explosion, so may fallout radiation. Large bodies of wind-thrown timber provide highly favorable conditions for the build-up of beetle populations, because green trees that have been blown over may live on for a while but can offer little resistance to the attack of insects. The same statement applies to radiation-damaged trees, which would afford an ideal substrate for the rapid growth of many arthropods and microorganisms.

Although scientific data in this field are scant, there exists at least one experimental observation that would support this contention. G. M. Woodwell, ecologist at the Brookhaven National Laboratory, studied the effects of chronic gamma radiation on an oak-pine forest on Long Island, New York. At distances from the radioactive cesium source where the oaks received 5 roentgens per day, the defoliation by insects was about five times as great as that observed in control areas. At these distances the oaks showed no overt signs of radiation damage in that both shoot expansion and leaf development were normal. Closer to the center, where the oaks had been severely injured by the radiation, the insect defoliation was about ten times as severe as in the control areas. Most of the insect damage was attributed to leaftiers, leaf rollers, leaf beetles, and loopers.

In a post-nuclear-attack situation, an explosive build-up of beetle or other insect populations would be further encouraged by the destruction of vertebrate populations. Predators such as woodpeckers, many of which readily survive storms and fires, would be almost completely eliminated by high-intensity radiation. Only those migrating from outside the fallout field would be available to begin building up a predator population. It takes years to build up a substantial woodpecker population, but an unchecked bark-beetle population can increase at a rate of 500 to 1 in a single generation. Furthermore, once an insect population has overwhelmed a forest, predator control becomes relatively insignificant.

A specific case in point is a study made on another forest pest, the spruce budworm. Although under normal circumstances birds are extremely important in controlling low endemic levels of spruce-budworm populations, during outbreaks the birds exercise only a minor influence. In New Brunswick, Canada, the budworm population increased eight-thousandfold, while its most responsive predator, the bay-breasted warbler, increased only twelvefold. The budworm population ultimately declined, but only because it had run out of food. In the stand studied, defoliation became severe in 1950, trees started to die in 1954, and tree mortality approached 100 per cent around 1960. Thus, it was the extensive defoliation and tree mortality, followed by the great outward emigrations of moths which accompanies these phenomena, rather than increased predation, which finally brought about the reduction of the budworm population.

In the case of the Engelmann spruce bark beetles, once a sufficiently large population had built up, and once the preferred food supply had been consumed, the beetles were forced to prey on healthy trees. This resulted in a temporary increase in beetle mortality since many a beetle succumbed to the pitch, but before long the attacked trees also sickened and offered little further resistance. The forest was overwhelmed and as the local food supply ran out, hordes of beetles migrated to other localities to repeat the process.

Actually the above story is oversimplified. The ecological relationships between insects and plants are more complicated in that not only food supply and insectivorous birds determine the rise and fall of all insect populations. Climatic factors, microbial parasites, and predation and parasitism by other invertebrates also play a significant role in keeping insect and other arthropod populations in check. In fact, as B. D. Burks, of the Bureau of Entomology and Plant Quarantine, has aptly summarized: "throughout their lives from egg to death, most insects are surrounded by others that are trying to eat them or lay their eggs in them or on them or to seize and carry them off to become food for their own developing brood. Many insects pillage the food their more industrious relatives have accumulated. While the interlopers grow fat, the helpless young that should have had the food are killed or die of starvation." Even mites of one species have recently been found to be attacked by mites of another species.

By and large, the control exercised by arthropods on their relatives tends to be specific. That is, any one arthropod parasitizes only one, or a few, other species of arthropods. In contrast, insectivorous frogs, lizards, birds, and mammals eat almost any small creature that moves. Furthermore, vertebrates tend to consume what is most readily available, and what is most readily available tends to be those insects whose populations have overcome the controls that normally keep them in check. Statistics bear out the significant contributions made by birds toward maintaining nature's balance. In farmyards in the Salt Lake Valley in 1910 and 1911, E. R. Kalmbach captured adult English sparrows returning to their nests and analyzed the content of their bills and throats. On the basis of these observations, Kalmbach estimated that the amount of food brought in at each trip by the adult birds amounted to an average of fifteen alfalfa weevil larvae or their equivalent of other insects. The adult sparrows averaged eleven trips per hour. Assuming that the young were fed twelve hours a day, a single brood of English sparrows would account for 1,980 larvae or their equivalent of other insect food. At the time these studies were undertaken, it was not uncommon to find farmyards with straw-thatched cattle sheds that supported a hundred or more nests of English sparrows. Such a colony of birds would devour daily a total of 198,000 alfalfa weevil larvae or other insect food. As the young remained in the nests for at least ten days, they would have eaten insect food equal to the volume of 1,980,000 weevil larvae during their nestling life

There are many instances of birds controlling outbreaks of coddling moths, brown-tail moths, gypsy moths, caterpillars, flies, beetles, and other insects. For example, woodpeckers have been known to decimate bark-beetle populations and thus prevent plagues like the one that struck the Engelmann spruce. However, as one noted student of these problems, F. E. L. Beal, has pointed out, "it would appear that the true function of the insectivorous birds is not so much to destroy this or that insect pest as it is to lessen the numbers of the insect tribe as a whole—to reduce to a lower level the great flood tide of insect life." E. R. Kalmbach has added that "flexibility of food habits and a tendency to prey on what is most abundant and easiest to capture make the bird world a highly mobile and responsive force for the reduction of any insect that may be inordinately abundant—significantly, the destructive insects are as a rule the most abundant ones."

The bird world is reinforced by a number of mammals such as bats, moles, shrews, skunks, armadillos, and grasshopper mice. Grasshopper mice and deer mice were conspicuous in their destruction of range caterpillars in New Mexico in 1913. Skunks were also found to contain remains in their droppings that indicated that 85 per cent of their food consisted of the pupae of this insect. Late in the pupal season, the localities that showed signs of skunk activities would be largely free of pupae. Frequently areas of four to five acres would have two thirds of the silken cocoon webs empty. In a section near Maxwell it was reported that only 5 per cent of the pupae remained undamaged. This was thought to be the result of attacks by mammals, including several species of mice, skunks, badgers, and even coyotes.

It should be clear by now that even though invertebrate parasites and predators play a very significant role in maintaining current balances, the presence of the insectivorous vertebrates is also crucial. There are three lines of defense against calamitous outbreaks of insect plagues. The first is made up of those predaceous and parasitic arthropods which live at the expense of their relatives; the second consists of the vertebrates whose more versatile food habits reduce any excess population that tends to get out of hand; the third is the rapid spread of microbial parasites leading to an epizootic. The last line of defense is most effective after a population has already exceeded its normal quota and has become crowded. There are also other pressures, some of which operate specifically against certain arthropods (e.g., the production of insect repellent or toxic substances by plants), and others that operate nonspecifically (e.g., adverse climatic conditions). An insect plague, as discussed above, may also run its course as a result of food shortages. In addition, and perhaps of greatest importance in considering the ecology of the United States, there are the efforts made by man to combat insect infestations.

Sometimes the first line of defense is nonexistent, or has become only partially established. This is the case for immigrants like the gypsy moth and the Japanese beetle which are still not in full equilibrium with their new surroundings in the United States. Even in the absence of the additional stress imposed by radiation, a dramatic flare-up of these well-known pests might suddenly occur. In other cases the first line of defense may become seriously weakened as a result of fallout. This is exemplified by the studies of a mixed population of predator and prey mites. At radiation doses higher than 3,000 roentgens but below 25,000 roentgens predator mites declined more rapidly than their cousins on whom they preyed. This led to a lowered mortality among the prey, with a corresponding prey population increase. The case is similar to the rise of European red mites in orchards all over the world as a result of the extensive use of DDT, which killed off their more sensitive insect predators, ladybird beetles.

Once the first line of defense is breached, the second line of defense (if fallout deposition has been sufficiently intense and widespread to reduce the vertebrates) would insure a population explosion, if food supplies were adequate. Sometimes even if the vertebrate population remained intact, the dramatic increase in preferred food supply (radiation-damaged plants) could permit insect populations to outrun their predators. This occurred in the case of the spruce budworm outbreaks described above.

Radiation from fallout deposited on marginal grasslands could have the same effect as overgrazing. A patchwork of vegetation and bare ground favors the population build-up of locusts in desert or semiarid country. If population density increases sufficiently the locusts develop longer wings as a result of crowding, and swarms may emigrate into cultivated lands, consuming everything in their path. For most insects, plague populations would be achieved within one to a few summers.

The third line of defense, the microbial parasites, becomes most significant when the explosion has already taken place and the proximity of large numbers of insects assures the rapid spread of parasites. Crowding of certain insects increases the incidence of diseases among them. In some situations the disease seems to appear as the result of the activation of a latent virus. In other cases, the stress of crowding lowers the host's resistance so that microorganisms normally present in the environment, including those in the insect's own gut, can produce disease. Radiation would not seriously weaken this third line of defense against the insects. If anything it might make it more effective by producing new mutants that possess a greater infectivity or pathogenicity or both. For this reason it is possible that some of the insect plagues might run their course within a single season.

Not only would the relationship between insects and their pathogens be altered, but also the relationships between plants and plant pathogens might be changed. Plants weakened by radiation succumb more readily to invasion by microorganisms. All pine seeds exposed to 5,000 roentgens failed to germinate in an experiment conducted by two Swedish scientists, while 1,000-roentgen doses permitted about a third of the seeds to germinate. However, these seedlings were weak, and all were killed by damping-off fungus. Survival of exposed plants following intense, widespread radiation is further jeopardized by the possible acceleration of mutation rates which might result in the production of new pathogenic mutants. New races of rusts, smuts, rots, scabs, blights, burns, galls, wilts, cankers, blotches, mildews, and other disease-producing organisms might appear following the widespread deposition of fallout, and these new races might give rise to others capable of attacking formerly resistant hosts, or inducing greater damage more rapidly in susceptible ones.

Probably more important than the possible increase in the pathogenicity of various disease-producing microorganisms would be the increase in the insect (and other invertebrate) populations. Insects influence plant diseases in many ways. Aphids, leafhoppers, and a number of other insects transmit virus diseases, and many insects are known to carry and transmit bacterial and fungal plant diseases. Some pathogens rely on insects as an alternate host in which to grow and multiply. Even insects and other invertebrates (e.g., nematodes) that do not transmit diseases themselves facilitate the spread of disease by making wounds on a plant through which fungi or bacteria may enter, or by weakening a plant so as to make it more susceptible to disease attack.

The reverse may also be true. Disease attack may weaken the

plant sufficiently to facilitate invasion by insects. The classic example of this is the Dutch elm disease in which an insect and a microbe act as a team. The smaller European elm bark beetle spreads the disease, and the fungus *Ceratostomella ulmi* provides more favorable breeding places for the beetle by weakening and killing healthy trees. Even in the absence of radiation, one may see history repeated if the newly invading bark beetle *Xylosandrus germanus* attacking oaks in the Eastern United States and the fungus *Endoconidiophora fagacaerum* causing oak wilt in the Central States become associated.

The Dutch elm disease illustrates another principle: the synergistic effect of double assault. The smaller European elm bark beetle is known to have become established in Boston as early as 1904, but it did little damage and was not considered a serious pest for a quarter of a century. In the absence of a natural mechanism of dissemination, the fungus *Ceratostomella ulmi* is not much of a threat. But the double assault of beetles and fungus has been disastrous for the American elms. Similarly, defoliation by the gypsy moth retards growth, but a single defoliation usually does not kill. Death usually results only from repeated defoliation, although young white pine trees and some other conifers frequently do die after a single stripping of the foliage. On the other hand, if defoliation occurs during long periods of drought, or if young emerging leaves from primary buds have been killed off earlier in the season by a late frost, then the added insult of insect defoliation is too much, and the tree dies. On the basis of these observations it would not be unreasonable to expect trees whose regenerative resilience has been seriously impaired by exposure to several thousand roentgens to succumb to a single defoliation by the gypsy moth.

It is clear, therefore, that fallout fields of several thousand roentgens are likely to place an overwhelming stress on terrestrial plants. First, even though many mature plants may survive exposure to 5,000 roentgens, they may be sterilized. Second, the upset in ecological balances exposes plants to a greatly increased twin threat of insect infestation and disease, at a time when they are least capable of resisting such an assault.

One ecological imbalance tends to lead to another. Large stands of killed trees are highly susceptible to forest fires. Some of the worst fires on record have occurred in localities of beetle-killed forests. The reverse also occurs: fire-damaged trees are often a favorite breeding ground for certain bark beetles. Even with this country's extensive fire-fighting organizations, several thousand square miles burn down each year. It is easy to imagine how with fire-fighting facilities severely handicapped or even nonexistent and large tracts of radiation-killed or insect-killed trees there could be larger and more destructive forest fires than have ever occurred on this continent.

Recovery from forest fires is a natural event, but recovery from forest fires in areas devastated by radiation, insects, or disease is another matter. Many of the adaptive devices that have evolved to insure regeneration or repopulation following a fire would probably be relatively ineffective following large doses of radiation. For example, many pine seeds are not released until the cones containing them are heated. Thus, a fire that destroys one generation of trees may sow the seeds for the next. In an irradiated forest, however, there may be no viable seed. Studies on the irradiated forest in Georgia indicate that whereas about 7,500 roentgens completely killed the loblolly pines, doses of only about 1,000 roentgens caused the trees to form abortive cones. Other studies indicate that conifer seeds already formed would also be killed or seriously handicapped at doses much lower than those required to kill the trees (spruce seeds are killed at doses of 1,000 roentgens). In addition, relatively low residual doses in the environment might also impede recovery. For this reason, reforestation following fires is not necessarily an automatic process in radiation-damaged forests.

It is not unreasonable to expect that a single twenty-megaton weapon would contaminate 4,800 square miles to the extent that the exposure would amount to several thousand roentgens over a few weeks. This dose would probably be high enough to kill coniferous forests (e.g., the spruce forests of the Western States), and place in serious jeopardy the deciduous forests (e.g., the oak-hickory forests of the East). This dose of fallout would probably also ruin the grasslands. Most herbaceous plants such as grasses and weeds are much more resistant to gamma radiation than are trees, but fallout would irradiate plants not only with gamma rays, but also with alpha and beta rays. The doses cited above refer to doses at three feet above ground. Actually, the doses at one sixteenth of an inch above a surface covered with fallout are likely to be at least ten times those at three feet above ground. This might prove to be extremely damaging to many herbaceous plants. Thus, the fallout from a single twenty-megaton bomb could readily devastate an area the size of the state of Connecticut.

Extensive local fallout would upset many of nature's balanced relationships. The most serious upset would stem from the build-up of insect populations as a result of providing the insects with large numbers of radiation-injured trees and other plants, while at the same time drastically reducing the vertebrate populations which normally help keep the insects in check. There are by far more kinds of insects than all other kinds of animals combined; therefore it is not possible to predict exactly which insects would be likely to achieve "plague" status. Certainly, on the basis of past experience, bark beetles, leaf beetles, and loopers are likely to become a problem. But so may the vast tribes of other well-known insect pests such as weevils, aphids, crickets, grasshoppers, leafhoppers, Japanese beetles, potato beetles, striped cucumber beetles, coddling moths, gypsy moths, San José scales, cabbage worms, tomato worms, wireworms, hornworms, cutworms, earworms, armyworms, jointworms, squash bugs, spittle bugs, stink bugs, lygus bugs, mealybugs, chinch bugs, borers, sawflies, Hessian flies, and thrips, as well as other prominent, or at the moment inconspicuous, insects which may suddenly bloom forth as a result of altered ecological forces.

Mushrooming insect populations are likely to spread from the radiation-damaged areas in which they arose, and, like the locusts of biblical times, wreak havoc in previously undamaged areas. Accompanying the insect plagues would be the plant diseases transmitted by insects, particularly those diseases which attack plants that have been injured or weakened by insect or radiation damage. The combined assault of radiation, insects, disease, and fire could temporarily strip off the plant cover of vast areas. If the attack is sufficiently widespread, it is conceivable that a few years later almost all the forests would have been destroyed, and most of the countryside would have become converted into marginal grasslands, if not actually stripped, leaving a naked earth to be ravaged by the ever-present forces of erosion.

12

ECOLOGICAL UPSETS: Climate and Erosion

The ecological imbalances that could be produced by extensive fallout have been described in the preceding chapter. These imbalances would be caused by the radiation emitted by the fallout. In addition, the simple act of injecting a large quantity of dirt and other matter into the atmosphere could also have profound consequences. First, fallout particles settling on snow would cause the snow to melt more rapidly. Under certain circumstances this could lead to disastrous floods. Second, and more important, injecting large quantities of small particles high into the astmosphere could produce marked changes in the weather, changes which under extreme conditions might initiate another ice age.

Let us examine these possibilities in somewhat more detail: Dirt particles on snow greatly enhance solar heat absorption by the snow cover. Farmers in northern and eastern Europe take advantage of this fact by spreading coal dust on snow-covered fields to insure early melt out, thereby prolonging the growing season. Irregular patterns of melting snow may also be observed in western Colorado, caused by dust blown in, presumably from Utah.

Thus, should a substantial amount of fallout settle in the mountains during the winter, and if the ground beneath the snow cover

136

is frozen, then the usual spring flood conditions would be seriously aggravated. Although at first glance this possibility seems somewhat academic, the fact that many communities are located in the valleys of rivers that flood regularly means that great havoc could be wrought by extensive fallout deposition upstream. The material spread over the countryside by a single twenty-megaton surface burst on soft soil could theoretically cover an area of more than 3,600 square miles to a depth of one millimeter.* One could readily envision that if sixty-six megatons were detonated in a broad belt from Pittsburgh to Cleveland, as was assumed by the 1959 Holifield Hearings, but late in the winter, that sizable areas of the snow-covered Appalachian Mountain Range leeward to the east might well become the source of devastating flood problems the following spring.

In addition to particles on the ground, the presence of small particles in the atmosphere could affect the weather in at least two ways. Particles in the lower atmosphere can act as nuclei for the condensation of water vapor, producing an increase in rain and snow; while particles in the stratosphere can act as a sky shield against the sun, producing colder weather on earth. The immediate effect of particles in the atmosphere was dramatically described by Colonel Lunger in his testimony before the Holifield Committee. On the evening following the 1952 MIKE shot, Colonel Lunger observed "an amber glow along the entire horizon. It was the most artificial thing I have ever seen and sensed in my life. We had displaced many millions of tons of coral debris that had been lifted up to forty and fifty thousand feet by the blast."

The phenomenon described by Colonel Lunger is reminiscent of what has been observed after volcanic eruptions. Among the most famous of these is the eruption of Krakatoa in 1883. The dust thrown up by this eruption caused brilliant sunsets all over the

---

* A twenty-megaton surface burst on soil would produce a crater 800 feet deep and 3,400 feet across, displacing a volume of 3.6×10^9 cubic feet. If one assumes that only 10 per cent of the displaced material is deposited over the countryside as small fallout particles (the rest comprising the crater lip, throw out, stem material, and material injected into the atmosphere), then 3.6×10^8 cubic feet would be involved. Theoretically, one cubic foot of fine particles could uniformly cover an area of about 300 square feet to a depth of one millimeter. Therefore, the material spread over the countryside by a twenty-megaton surface burst could theoretically cover in excess of 10^{11} square feet to a depth of one millimeter, i.e., about 3,600 square miles. Although fallout is not deposited uniformly, a cover less than one millimeter is probably still sufficient to exert a pronounced effect. In addition, the assumption that only 10 per cent of the crater material is deposited as local fallout is probably too low.

world for the next few years. More important, the dust acted as a shield against the sun's rays, reflecting a relatively small but significant amount of energy back out into space. In France, measurements of the radiation intensities of sunlight were taken which showed a decrease of almost 10 per cent for the next three years. The consequent reduction in the amount of energy absorbed by the earth produced a cooling effect which manifested itself as unusually cold weather in many parts of the world.

The explosion of Krakatoa was the greatest since 1783, when Mt. Asama in Japan produced the most frightful eruption on record. In the Krakatoa eruption, the quantity of earth blown up into the atmosphere amounted to a cubic mile, according to one estimate, most of which descended in the surrounding Straits of Sunda. The fine particles took about three months to reach Western Europe. The world's mean temperature declined by about 1° Fahrenheit in 1884, the year following the Krakatoa eruption. However, probably some of the cold weather can be attributed to causes other than volcanic dust.

A more dramatic example of volcanic activity influencing weather occurred in the early part of the nineteenth century. A series of volcanic eruptions, beginning around 1808 and culminating with the eruption of Mt. Tomboro, on Soembawa Island in Indonesia, on April 7 to 12, 1815, resulted in a memorable cold spell the world over. The Tomboro eruption killed 56,000 people and blew up so much dust that for three days there was darkness up to three hundred miles away. The following year, 1816, became famous in folklore as "eighteen hundred and froze-to-death," "poverty year," and "the year without a summer."

Volcanic dust is probably the most important single factor in determining the fluctuations in world temperature. Other natural factors also contribute significantly, but an envelope of volcanic dust in the upper atmosphere probably exerts the most profound cooling effect on the earth's surface.* W. J. Humphreys, meteoro-

---

* It is not certain whether volcanic dust reflects the sun's radiation directly, or whether some more indirect mechanisms might also be involved. Dr. H. Wexler, former Director of Research of the United States Weather Bureau, has suggested that the volcanic dust particles may also serve as nuclei for ice-crystal formation in the atmosphere, causing an increase in the total high-level cloud cover. Other effects are also conceivable. In any case, particles in the air reduce the surface temperature: for example, on September 25 and 26, 1950, the solar radiation received at Washington, D.C., was only 52 per cent of normal, even though it was a cloudless day. This reduction in solar radiation was caused by a pall of smoke emanating from extensive forest fires in western Canada which covered the eastern United

logical physicist of the United States Weather Bureau, has stated that since the beginning of reliable meteorological records at the end of the eighteenth century, the temperature of the earth has been lowered by as much as perhaps 1° as a result of volcanic explosions violent enough to put dust into the upper atmosphere. Furthermore, if volcanic explosions during this period had been three or four times more numerous than they actually were, the average temperature probably would have been about 2° to 3½° lower than was observed, which is low enough, if continued for a long period of time, to depress the snow line 300 meters (almost 1,000 feet), and thus initiate a moderate ice age.

A reduction of only 10 per cent in the amount of solar radiation striking the earth's surface is sufficient to result in a world-wide cooling of about 11° if maintained over a long period of time. The glaciation that would result from this great a temperature drop would equal or exceed the most extensive experienced in any ice age. The eruption of Mt. Katmai in 1912 resulted in an over-all 10 per cent reduction of solar radiation. Data obtained on this dust cover permitted Humphreys to calculate that the amount of dust required to cause a 20 per cent reduction in the amount of solar radiation is "astonishingly small"; only about 1/1000 of a cubic mile would suffice to cover the earth.

The amount of material gouged out of the ground by a single twenty-megaton bomb detonated on soil is approximately 1/40 of a cubic mile. This means one hundred such detonations (a total of two thousand megatons) would gouge out somewhat over two cubic miles. If one assumes that 5 per cent of this material were injected into the stratosphere as relatively small particles (less than 20 microns in diameter), then two thousand megatons would inject 1/10 cubic mile into the stratosphere. Of this stratospheric material, perhaps only 1 per cent might consist of very small particles (less than 2 microns in diameter), which are of greatest importance in the cooling process; therefore two thousand megatons could produce about 1/1000 of a cubic mile of fine dust particles, sufficient to reduce the solar radiation by 20 per cent. The reduction in solar radiation caused by the presence of fine atomic ash in the stratosphere would not immediately bring about a change in

States, Canada, and Europe. It was estimated that during the two days the loss of radiant energy lowered the maximum temperature in Washington by 5° to 10° Fahrenheit.

world-wide temperature, since the oceans act as a buffer. However, over large land masses the effect would probably be more immediate.

The question arises: How long would this cold weather last? This depends not only on the number of particles in the stratosphere, but also on their rate of descent. Physicist R. U. Ayres of the Hudson Institute has calculated that two thirds of the 2 micron particles would have descended by the end of a year and a half. Therefore, a year and a half after a six-thousand-megaton war (three thousand megatons on each side) there would still be sufficient debris in the stratosphere to reduce the solar radiation by 20 per cent. This implies that the cold spell would last several years, but one can only speculate on the meaning of this cold spell. If the temperature drop averaged out to about 7° over eastern North America, it would mean that the weather in Washington, D.C., would be more like the weather currently observed in Ottawa, Canada.* This would have profound implications for agriculture: the wheat belt, for example, would be shifted about five hundred miles south. If, on the other hand, the temperature drop averaged out to about 14°, it is likely that there would be years like 1816, the "year without a summer." A drop of 14° means that in New York City, for example, temperatures in the middle of July would be like those in the middle of May.

Presumably after a few years, as the atomic dust settled, the weather would return to normal. However, there is the remote possibility that the cold spell might last long enough to initiate a vicious cycle. The presence of a white snow cover on the surface of the earth greatly increases the reflection of solar radiation back out into space. Whereas water and land surfaces tend to reflect from 3 to 35 per cent of the solar radiation, a snow cover tends to reflect between 50 and 85 per cent. The snow cover does not appreciably inhibit the release of heat from the surface of the earth out into space. Thus, one can readily envision the mechanism proposed by W. J. Humphreys, whereby the land surfaces heat up barely at all throughout most of the year, while water surfaces near the Arctic tend to freeze up more and more each winter. If a sufficiently large part of the North Atlantic were to freeze over to deflect the Gulf Stream, then Europe would freeze over com-

* In eastern North America, decreasing the temperature by 1° is equivalent to moving seventy miles north.

pletely. (England is as far north as Labrador, but the west winds picking up heat from the Gulf Stream keep the continent warm.) Although the advent of an ice age following a thermonuclear war seems unlikely, it is not until the mechanisms of ice-age formation are clearly understood that one can positively rule out this possibility.

If the detonation of a large number of surface bursts should lead to an ice age, then the distortion of nature would last for millennia. A number of other upsets would also follow: the weather pattern in many parts of the world would be altered, the level of the oceans would subside as more and more water became trapped by the glaciers, mass population migrations would alter the current social and political make-up. However, even in the absence of so cataclysmic an event as the creation of an ice age, the cascading of natural upsets following a nuclear disaster might lead to profound changes. The recovery of nature is by no means a foregone conclusion. There is a very real possibility that if the United States were hit hard enough by a nuclear attack most of the country would be converted into a barren desert.

The essence of the problem is this: If the plant cover is destroyed because the radiation-damaged plants succumb to insects, to unusually harsh weather, or to other forces, will the exposed earth erode irreversibly? Under certain circumstances the original plant cover can be restored. Under other circumstances, a plant cover may be restored but may be different from the one that originally characterized the area. A third possibility is that there would be a downward spiral in which various factors would combine to aggravate an already bad situation, producing an environment too hostile to permit the natural re-establishment of a plant cover. Certainly there is sufficient historical experience to indicate that if erosion became a continental, rather than a local, problem the United States would be likely to suffer the same fate as North Africa, the Middle East, and other parts of the world that eroded into desert.

As we have seen, local fallout is likely to trigger a chain of events that would lead to insect plagues, which, of course, would contribute to the destruction of the plant cover. However, insect plagues would not arise if the climate became sufficiently cold. Yet ground bursts, which produce local fallout, are also likely to produce enough stratospheric dust to cause severe cooling. Cold weather slows up the development of many insects in summer and greatly increases insect mortality in winter. Moreover, many radiation-damaged plants, which would serve as a stimulus to an expanding insect population by providing a choice food supply, would probably be killed by the cold weather. For these reasons the insect populations would be drastically reduced by the cold weather and would either not build up at all, or would do so only following the return of normal temperatures. On the other hand, if an insect and its host had a sufficient range, then a large insect population might build up in the south, migrating north as climatic conditions became favorable.

In those parts of the country where cooling effects were serious enough to prevent the build-up of insect populations, radiation-damaged trees and other plants might be unable to cope with the additional stress of unseasonable frosts and shortened growing seasons. The ecologist R. B. Platt has observed in his studies of the irradiated forest in northern Georgia that even under normal conditions in spring radiation-damaged trees break dormancy anywhere from one to eight weeks later than do nonirradiated controls, depending upon the extent of injury. This would mean that many fallout-damaged trees would break dormancy two months later, at a time when the growing season may be perhaps two months shorter.

Radiation, cold weather, and insects offer the most widespread insult to the plant cover, but there would be other serious stresses as well. Some of these, such as disease and fire following insect devastation, have already been discussed in the previous chapter. In addition, there would follow erosion, floods, and drought, while thousands of square miles would probably be destroyed within hours after an attack as a result of the heat and blast released by the nuclear detonations. Blast damage would probably not be very important because blast areas would most likely be too limited to have a significant effect on nature, and most plants have a tremendous capacity to regenerate (a single cell originally derived from the stem of a tobacco plant has been shown to regenerate an entire tobacco plant). This is borne out by studies on atom-blasted islets at Eniwetok. Heat, on the other hand, could ignite very large tracts of forest. These fires would be worse than ordinary forest fires in that a large forest fire takes days and even weeks to cover a large area, whereas a twenty-megaton low air burst would ignite many small fires in a 1,000-square-mile area *simultaneously*, resulting in a total burn-out of the area. Even at its peak, the Tillamook fire in Oregon was moving along its fifteen-mile front at an average rate of two miles an hour,* a rate of burning that permitted birds and many mammals to get out of the way. Furthermore, large tracts of forest remained untouched: in the very center, a 25,000-acre tract was spared.

How fast is a destroyed plant cover likely to regenerate? In the first place, some initial reproduction of plant life is virtually assured. Certain plants are highly radioresistant and these might initially displace more common, but also more sensitive, plants. Second, the soil constitutes a reservoir of seeds which, because they are underground and because of the inhomogeneity of fallout deposition, would survive. They would need only favorable ecological circumstances to germinate and produce normal plants. These plants would most likely be those currently considered weeds, but they would be admirably suited for establishing a plant cover. This process has actually been observed under natural conditions, and in the course of solving problems associated with erosion. Third, many perennial grasses and ferns, as well as other plants, have shoot meristems which are at or below the ground surface. Additional shielding provided by snow, other plants, or rocks, houses, bridges, and the like would insure the initial survival of some of these meristems capable of vegetative reproduction. Whether the plants coming up from seeds or shielded meristems would prosper and repopulate the earth, or whether they would succumb to assault by insects, microbes, fires, erosion, or adverse climatic events would be determined largely by how rapidly the ecosystem can reconstitute itself.

Normally, if the vegetation is destroyed, nature restores the balance. Terrestrial plant successions after fires, for example, follow some well-established principles. In many parts of the eastern United States, burned-over areas are soon covered by grasses and large annual herbs such as milkweeds, goldenrods, asters and eve-

---

* The Tillamook forest fire burned a total of 486 square miles of virgin Douglas fir. From August 14, 1933, until August 24, the fire burned about 63 square miles. On the 24th, the humidity dropped rapidly to 26 per cent and hot gale-force winds from the east sprang up. During the next twenty hours the fire raged over an additional 420 square miles at a rate of about twenty-one square miles per hour along a fifteen-mile front. The fire stopped as the wind ceased and a thick, wet blanket of fog drifted in from the ocean.

ning primroses. In wetter areas, sedges of various species, water hemlock, blue-eyed grass, and rushes make their appearance. With time, the saplings of shrubs and trees begin to grow. Among them, sumac, aspen, poplar, blackberries, hawthorn, black locust, red and white cedars, and mulberry begin to fill up the open fields. These, in turn, are replaced by taller trees such as red maples and willows in moist areas, or aspens and gray birch, or locusts, oaks, and hickories in dry areas. Ultimately, the oaks and hickories tend to completely dominate the biotic community of plants, the community having once again achieved its stabilized "climax" vegetation. Such a climax community, the culmination of a succession of communities of the type just described, may consist of other trees, such as beech, hemlock, and maple, and it may evolve via different intermediate stages. However, it should be understood that an almost predictable sequence of plant communities arises to restore the former balance in any given location. The return of the climax flora is accompanied by a similar sequence of events tending to restore the climax fauna.

In order for natural repair to occur, other ecological elements must remain essentially intact. A decrease either in rainfall or soil fertility can drastically inhibit the kind of recovery discussed above. A. H. Benton and W. E. Werner, in their book, *Principles of Field Biology and Ecology*, provide an example of a biotic community diverted from its climax forest as a result of a combination of human activities and fire. Between Albany and Schenectady, in eastern New York State, there is an area of sandy soil that covers a strip some twenty miles long and five or six miles wide. Much of this land was once covered with a climax forest of white pine. As a result of agricultural activity, the trees were cut, and parts of the sandy soil were farmed. Fires occurred frequently, burning what little humus had built up, and eventually the whole area became a sandy plain. White pine, which could not tolerate the fires, was replaced by pitch pine, which could. Today the pitch pines grow scattered about as in a savanna, while shrubs of bear oak, dwarf cherries, staghorn, and smooth sumacs comprise the main vegetation underneath.

The most extreme cases of denudation of a plant cover are found around certain ore-smelting towns where the plants are poisoned by toxic products. In one such area, near Copper Hills, Georgia, the release of sulphur dioxide fumes from the copper-smelting operations during the first part of this century denuded the local countryside of its vegetation. The high temperatures and rainfall in the area favored rapid erosion, so that thirty years after the introduction of modern refining methods, which contain the noxious fumes, the area was still barren. Attempts to reforest the area have not yet succeeded. Erosion and the changes in micro-climate that accompany it have combined with the original destructive forces to create a desert in which the land has become too hostile for even artificial reconstruction by conventional techniques.

Thus, the comforting assumption that nature tends to restore its former balance following the destruction of vegetation is not always borne out by experience. In many instances nature arrives instead at a new balance, a balance obviously quite hostile to man.

Nowhere is this more clearly illustrated than in North Africa. Fertile fields once covered most of Egypt, whereas now they are confined almost entirely to the Nile Valley. Beneath the Sahara Desert, covered by thick layers of sand, are traces of dense forest which, less than two thousand years ago, made a rich colony of what is now barren soil and arid land. At El Djem, hidden partly beneath the sands, are the ruins of the great town of Thysdrus, noted for its stadium built to hold 60,000 spectators. Like other buried cities scattered across the North African desert, these ruins are a mute reminder of the fact that this region was once "the granary of the Roman empire." Since Roman times, well over 12,000,000 acres of forest have disappeared in Morocco alone, as a result of fire and overgrazing by sheep and goats.

The cause of the decline of North Africa is popularly attributed to climatic changes, the theory being that the area became hotter and drier and the people were forced to abandon a thriving civilization. However, some geologists, after carefully weighing the evidence, have challenged the conclusion that the climate has changed in any important way since Roman times. Although climatological factors may also have contributed, it was man who destroyed the balance of nature responsible for maintaining soil fertility and moisture.

Why is it that under certain circumstances, the plant cover is unable to regenerate itself, thus setting the stage for serious erosion? To answer this question, let us first take an extreme example, the destruction of tropical rain forests. In general, the equatorial soil is poor: forests can exist in these regions only because they are part of a balanced cycle. All that the forest produces is returned to the forest. The organic matter that falls from the trees constitutes the humus that the forest requires. When man cuts down all the trees to make room for crops, the soil is laid bare and, deprived of shade, heats up. An increase in soil temperature increases the rate of decomposition of organic matter. Organic nitrogen is converted to soluble ammonia and nitrates, which the rains quickly leach away. Roger Bouillene, Director of the Botanical Institute and Garden at the University of Liège, has calculated that a rise in temperature from 77° to 78.8° Fahrenheit may increase the loss of nitrogen by fifteen to twenty pounds per acre per year. With the fertility of the soil destroyed, an irreversible change from forest to desert can be initiated.

Although the tropical rain forests are more susceptible to this type of destruction than are the leafy forests of the temperate zones, the change from forest to grassland to desert has occurred in many parts of the world, largely as a result of man's activities. Vegetation, soil, and microclimate form an interrelated dynamic complex which may be upset by any number of factors directly or indirectly attributable to nuclear war. The destruction of the plant cover, for example, immediately creates a much more hostile environment, an environment which heats up much more when the weather is hot, cools much more when it is cold, and which generally provides much less water. According to a study conducted in the north of Germany, if one simply removed the hedges along the fields, the increased evaporation caused by wind would be great enough to require one third more annual rainfall to compensate for the loss of the hedges. The presence of the hedges probably increased the grain yields by 20 per cent.

In the United States and other parts of the world, extensive use of shelter belts reduces evaporation and also conserves soil moisture by trapping snow and reducing runoff. A canopy of forest trees maintains a higher humidity, lowers high temperatures, and, in general, dramatically reduces the soil water loss by evaporation underneath. For example, a study conducted some years after the Tillamook forest fire compared a tract of forest that had remained intact with the surrounding burn area, which was covered with weeds and shrubs. The study showed that the area covered with weeds and shrubs was 10° hotter on the hottest day, 2° colder on the coldest night, and after ten days of drought showed not only a significantly lower relative humidity in the area but also a lowered soil moisture content. Perhaps most important was that the soil of the burn area contained about 20 per cent less organic material, and only about two fifths as much available phosphorus as did the soil of the intact forest.

Other studies have shown that under full shade, soil-surface temperatures remain cooler than air temperatures, even during the hottest part of the day, in contrast to unshaded soils, which are always warmer than the air only a few millimeters above ground. The difference between the surface temperature of thinly shaded and exposed dry, gray soil, when measured in the early afternoon of a clear day, exceeded 20°. A black, dry exposed surface was 25° hotter. In winter, on the other hand, dry soil is more prone to frost since the lower its moisture content, the poorer its heat conductivity. Clearly, a dry, exposed soil surface provides a very rigorous microenvironment.

Changing the microclimate in the grasslands can profoundly influence the rate of reproduction of certain insects. Grasshopper plagues originate not where the vegetation is lush, but in areas that form a mosaic of plants and bare soil. Similarly, the European rabbit thrives in areas of depleted, eroded soil. A build-up of these plant-eating animals can lead to overgrazing and the destruction of the remaining plants. Overgrazed plants are less able to cope with drought conditions. This was observed in Nebraska during the dry years in the early 1930's. Native grasses in long-overgrazed prairie, even though protected during recovery, wilted much more than did plants in adjacent prairie that had not been grazed. The leaves rolled or folded, and many of the lower ones dried and lost their green color. Studies showed that overgrazed plants develop poor root systems because whenever 50 per cent or more of the top of a grass plant has been removed, root growth stops completely and will not resume until there has been adequate shoot recovery six to eighteen days later. It is for this reason that overgrazed plants succumb readily to drought.

It is not surprising, therefore, to find that where grasslands were excessively challenged by overgrazing, the grasses were replaced by creosote bushes, mesquite, and cactus, forming a desert community. In Holland, the critical factor in sand-dune erosion proved to be grazing by rabbits. When the rabbits were eliminated as a result of disease (myxomatosis), erosion ceased to be a serious problem and the dune-fixing vegetation suddenly spread dramatically over the dune surfaces. Similarly, in Australia, land that had been previously classed as desert turned into grassland following the elimination of the rabbits.

Fallout, like overgrazing, would either create the kind of mosaic favorable to the build-up of grasshoppers, or it would stress the grasses so that they would be unable to survive severe unseasonable frosts, fire, or drought. This would be particularly true for the marginal grasslands throughout the Mountain and West Central States. Stripping the prairies of their grasses would subject them to wind erosion.*

One of America's leading ecologists, Paul B. Sears, has pointed out that "erosion, like many another curse of humanity, grows by what it feeds on." As the wind removes the fertile covering from one field, it destroys the vegetative covering on the next by inundating it with dust. The amount of dust that may be transported by winds is phenomenal. One need recall only the giant dust storms emanating from the dust bowl of the 1930's to appreciate this fact. Early in May 1934, hot, dry weather, followed by a strong wind, created a giant dust cloud about 1,800 miles wide, which struck New York City on May 11. The *New York Times* reported that "yellow dust, driven before a westerly wind, swept over the Eastern Seaboard region from Canada to far south of Washington. This phenomenon, never before experienced in Eastern America, was caused by a wind-driven fog of soil particles that came from drought-stricken areas." One estimate indicated that the cloud contained 300,000,000 tons of topsoil blown off the Central States and sprinkled over half the nation. The fine particles trebled the density of New York's atmosphere, veiling the sun for about five hours and requiring lights to be turned on in the middle of the day.

Serious as the dust-bowl problem was in the 1930's, it might be dwarfed by nuclear-attack dust-bowl problems. Much larger areas could be involved, resulting in an increased frequency and severity

* Soils with 80 per cent or more of fine sand are very vulnerable to erosion. Sand soils move readily when wind speeds six inches above ground exceed eleven miles per hour. This occurs when wind velocities at four and a half feet above ground exceed fourteen miles per hour. Winds exceeding these velocities are common in the Great Plains. Furthermore, the relatively high organic-matter content of the Great Plains soil accentuates their susceptibility to wind erosion.

of dust storms, and such dust storms might be particularly noxious because the dust would probably contain substantial amounts of long-lived radioactive fallout products, such as radioactive strontium and cesium.

The formation of a dust bowl is in itself by no means an irreversible phenomenon. In some areas of the dust bowl the dust, erosion, and extreme lack of moisture, plus the overgrazing and grasshopper hordes, killed off so much plant life that on ungrazed land it reduced the percentage of plant cover in a five-year period from 90 per cent to about 25 per cent, and on overgrazed land from 80 per cent to almost zero within four years. Yet, between 1940 and 1942 both kinds of land made a complete recovery.

Vigorous efforts can restore the productivity of even dry, infertile land. The state of Israel has conducted a vigorous land-reclamation program, including the draining of about seventy square miles of marshland and the irrigation of about five hundred square miles of arid land. As a result of these efforts, Israel was able to double the land under productive cultivation. The events in this part of the world illustrate the twin problem of deserts and swamps that may be created once unfavorable ecological balances bring about unchecked, accelerated erosion. The Huleh Basin, at the head of the Jordan Valley, was a fertile and thickly populated area in Roman times. This, and other areas at the eastern end of the Mediterranean, began to decline in productivity during the fading of the Byzantine Empire, about 1,300 years ago. The Huleh Basin became a dismal swamp—a focus of malaria infection —as a result of the deposition of sediments from eroding uplands to the north which progressively filled in the northern end of Lake Huleh. The successful reclamation of the area is a triumph of modern technology.

It should be recognized, however, that the Israeli experience may not be applicable after a nuclear attack. The Israelis had not only considerable and skilled manpower, but also very substantial material help from other countries. If much of the economy remained intact after a nuclear attack, the Israeli feat could probably be duplicated in this country. However, if the surviving population were too weak, or too small, and if no outside aid materialized, the country would be unable to check the erosive decay.

Thus far we have considered primarily wind erosion. Equally

important is water erosion on hilly or mountainous terrain. Plants on slopes soften the impact of raindrops by intercepting them on leaves or on litter under the plants, while organic matter and roots improve conditions of infiltration and thereby reduce runoff. Many of the factors we discussed earlier in relation to the retention of soil moisture by a plant cover also relate to reducing soil erosion. Plant roots tend to hold soil in place; in their absence rains leach out the minerals and wash the soil off the surface, first downhill, then downstream. Soil not washed off the surface may become compacted by the rain instead. This compaction reduces the ability of the soil to absorb water, resulting in increased runoff which, if sufficiently rapid, causes floods. Furthermore, as we have already seen in connection with the Huleh Basin, deposition is the complement of erosion. The soil particles carried downstream are deposited wherever the water speed diminishes sufficiently for the particles to settle out. This results in the silting up of reservoirs and irrigation systems. In the case of floods, the particles are deposited on the flood banks. At first this deposition actually enriches the valley with the topsoil carried down from upstream. However, if erosion is sufficiently severe, more and more of the soil that is deposited will consist of less fertile subsoil, until finally the flood plains may also become unproductive, having become inundated with infertile subsoil carried down from the destroyed land upstream.

The extent of erosion following a nuclear attack would depend largely on how quickly a devastated area could regenerate a plant cover. Survival of the ecosystem would depend on meteorological factors such as wind, precipitation, and temperature, and on geological factors such as the nature of the terrain and of the soil. For example, a flat plain with much of its humus left intact in a not-too-windy area of adequate rainfall would probably reconstitute itself rapidly, returning to its former climax community within one to a few years. On the other hand, if most of the humus were destroyed, either a strong wind or rains on the side of a slope would complete the denuding of the earth's fertile covering. The more unstable ecosystems, such as the marginal grasslands, would therefore be likely to succumb to the stresses placed on them by nuclear war.

An example of erosion culminating in a man-made desert is found in Syria. W. C. Lowdermilk, former Assistant Chief of the

Soil Conservation Service, describes the case of "the hundred dead cities." Between Alleppo, Hama, and Antioch there is an area of about 1,500 square miles of rolling limestone country which flourished until the seventh century. Then a series of invasions, first by the Persian Army, then, more disastrously, by nomads, wrought destruction and caused the methods for conserving soil and water to fall into disuse. Today one may still find the ruins of over a hundred former towns, "stark skeletons in beautifully cut stone, standing high on bare rock."

There is a popular misconception that a desert is a place that is very hot all the time. It is true that the barrenness of a desert causes it to heat up more when the sun is shining on it, but a desert can also be a very cold place.* The Syrian case is of interest because Alleppo is no farther south than Norfolk, Virginia, and the climate of Syria is comparable to the climate in much of the central and southeastern United States, although the mean annual rainfall is more comparable to Iowa or Illinois.

Meteorological conditions in the United States are really not very different from conditions in those parts of the world that have suffered calamitous erosion. As a matter of fact, some of the worst climate in the world is found over most of the United States. The climate of the West Central and Rocky Mountain States is rugged, and in many areas—from the Badlands in the Dakotas, to the Mojave Desert in southern California—the climate is frequently clearly hostile. East of the Rocky Mountains changes in temperature of up to 50° within a twelve-hour period are not uncommon, as warm tropical air masses coming from the south are displaced by cold polar air masses sweeping in from Arctic Canada. Much of this variability stems from the fact that, unlike Europe and North Africa, North America has no east-west mountain ranges to deflect these air masses. E. R. Biel, former Chairman of the Department of Meteorology at Rutgers University, has pointed out that even in the Northeast "the tropical heat conditions of our summers" cause the water requirements of plants to be very high. Biel points out, however, that we are fortunate that the tropical air masses from the south generally consist of marine air carrying enormous masses of precipitable water. This means that much of

* For example, the Great Basin Desert that extends north from southern Nevada and southern Utah may be subjected to killing frosts any month of the year; and in fall, winter, and spring frosts occur almost every night, often accompanied by bitter cold.

the United States is spared those desiccating and dust-laden air masses which are such a liability on other continents.

However, a nuclear attack could cancel out this fortuitous situation, as large areas of the United States became stripped of their plant cover. There is evidence to indicate that clouds that form over deserts are less likely to shed their moisture than are clouds formed over grasslands.* Thus, a vicious cycle could be initiated: land stripped of its plant cover as a result of nuclear attack would not only lose its fertility, but might also be deprived of adequate moisture and therefore have little chance to recover.

Mesopotamia stands out as the classical model of irreversible destruction visited upon a society by ecological devastation following a fatal war. For over 6,000 years the valleys of the Tigris and the Euphrates were a spawning ground of human civilization and progress. This was true in spite of the fact that Mesopotamia was repeatedly invaded and conquered. Babylonians, Assyrians, Persians, Macedonians, Parthians, Romans, and others, conquered part or all of the region. Then, in the middle of the thirteenth century came the Mongol invasion under Hulagu Khan, grandson of Genghis Khan, which, unlike earlier conquests, succeeded in destroying the country. The week after the surrender of Baghdad, 800,000 people were put to the sword. The earthen works on which the irrigation system depended were destroyed, and the canal system on which the land depended fell into ruin. As usual, war was followed by famine and epidemic diseases, which, coupled with the initial slaughter, left the survivors too weak to repair the complex irrigation system. The area that had been so productive rapidly turned into desert, and there followed a continuing struggle between the city and the nomads who roamed the impoverished countryside. Although millions of Mesopotamians survived, the "cradle of civilization" was no longer significant to the mainstream of human advancement. Mesopotamia's fate is in some ways most similar to what may be expected as a result of nuclear attack. Because of the staggering loss of both lives and resources, ecological destruction could not be checked, and a technologically advanced society was permanently destroyed.

* Although this evidence is far from conclusive, it is supported by other observations, also not conclusive as yet, which indicate that the presence of forests actually increase annual rainfall.

"Unto the Third and to the Fourth Generation"

The physical and psychological scars of a nuclear trauma are likely to be discernible for more than a century. Alterations in the genetic structure of individuals as a result of irradiation, and alterations in the cultural structure of a society as a result of a nuclear cataclysm, are likely to perpetuate themselves for many generations.

In a sense, these are analogous phenomena. Genetic information, in the case of man, directs the sequence of events in which a single cell, the fertilized egg, grows and multiplies to form the 25,000,000,000,000 cells that make up an adult human being. Culture entails a *paragenetic* means of transmitting information from one generation to the next. The cultural information passed on from generation to generation determines the interactions between individual human beings and the societies they form.

The farmer, the merchant, the manufacturer, may be compared to chromosomes: each contains a special body of information, which is transmitted to future individuals. Each unit of information—each fact, idea, value, memory—that is passed on to the next generation can be considered analogous to a gene. It follows that when the organization of a society is disrupted by a trauma, members of the society may pass on the effects of this shock to succeeding generations, so that individuals who were never themselves exposed to the catastrophe might inherit a legacy of psychological damage. When the genetic machinery of human cells is disrupted—for example, by ionizing radiation—a legacy of mutations is transmitted to succeeding generations. Thus, while the long-term social and cultural effects of a nuclear attack might be discussed in a chapter on social consequences, the striking analogy between the post-disaster genetic processes and the anticipated effects on societal organization justifies dealing with both subjects here.

A human cell is like an industrial complex, in the center of which is a factory (the cell's nucleus), which is responsible for running the industrial complex. Within the factory is a library in which is stored both the information for running the industrial complex and the information necessary to build another factory. The library's bookcases are like the chromosomes in the cell's nucleus—human nuclei normally contain forty-six chromosomes—and just as each book in the bookcase is made up of information in the form of printed letters, recent research has shown that genetic information is transmitted by means of a four-letter alphabet.

Each genetic "letter" is actually a chemical substance called a nucleotide, and each genetic "word" (at least those dealing with instructions for building specific proteins) consists of three letters, with each word designating a specific amino acid. A "sentence" consisting of a string of nucleotides forming a polymer of nucleic acid designates a specific sequence of amino acids. This sequence of amino acids comprises a protein, one of the fundamental building blocks of all living matter. The sentences of the genetic language are much longer than ours and there is no space between each of the three-letter words. This means that if a single letter drops out in the middle of a sentence, the meaning of the remaining part of the sentence is altered.* Any such deletion, or any other change, constitutes a mutation. If a mutation involves substituting a single letter, then a single amino acid may be changed in a protein. This altered protein may be only slightly different from

* For example, if the end of a sentence consisted of four sets of the genetic word TAC, i.e., TAC-TAC-TAC-TAC, and if the first T were to drop out, the end of the sentence would then read ACT-ACT-ACT-AC, the last being an incomplete two-letter word.

the original, or it might be very different. If, instead of a substitution, a deletion is involved, then the rest of the sentence may produce a nonsense protein. In any case, it becomes apparent that there is only a small possibility that the altered information might produce something more useful than the original, and that the chances are very much greater that the vast majority of mutations are destructive.

Mutations may arise spontaneously in nature, or they may be induced artificially. A number of grossly harmful mutations in man have been studied, and many of these seem to appear with a spontaneous frequency of about one new mutation per hundred thousand gametes (sperms or eggs). If one considers the sum of these grossly harmful mutations, then the spontaneous-mutation rate involves one gamete in a hundred. The geneticist H. J. Muller has estimated that the rate of *all types* of mutations in man involves about one gamete in ten; that is, every tenth sperm or egg carries a newly acquired mutation. It is probable that many, if not most, of these so-called spontaneous mutations in nature are caused by background radiation from natural occurring radioactive substances and cosmic rays, and it is now agreed that *any* increase in radiation exposure will increase the load of mutations that the human species carries.

The difficulty arises in assessing potential radiation damage in quantitative terms. One of the problems is deciding when a gene is truly harmful. Some mutations, such as those responsible for the death of young infants, are clearly deleterious, but since these individuals are rapidly eliminated, in the long run such mutant genes may do less harm to a whole population than less drastic, but still deleterious, genes, such as those responsible for lowered intelligence. Or, a mutant gene may be responsible for the loss of some synthetic capacity, yet still be advantageous: the loss of the ability to make pigment in the furs of rabbits—which produces a white coat—although disadvantageous to a rabbit inhabiting a brown-leafed forest floor, is advantageous to one inhabiting the snowy Arctic. Thus, a gene that is deleterious in one environment becomes useful in another.

With human beings the matter is even more complex, because man's environment is not only natural, but social as well. For example, a defect like myopia would be detrimental to a hunter but, if anything, helpful to a watchmaker. Therefore, instead of selecting for one perfect superman type, "diversifying selection" acting on a human population favors many types.* A population that abounds in genetic variety has a better chance to survive and prosper in a complex environment than does a genetically uniform population; variety is one way of exploiting the environment more fully.

By and large, however, beneficial mutations appear to be the rare exception, and so the problem in estimating genetic damage from radiation is how to calculate the extent of damage incurred. Calculations (see Appendix, pages 191-2) based on some of the more recent experiments on mice indicate that the acute radiation dose required to double the spontaneous mutation rate is of the order of 30 roentgens. A chronic dose, that is, if the radiation is given slowly over a long period of time, is only about a fourth as effective as an acute dose. Thus, for chronic irradiation the doubling dose is in the neighborhood of 120 roentgens.

At this point let us consider two hypothetical human populations, each consisting of a million individuals exposed to nuclear radiation from external sources, such as fallout on the ground. Assume that population A received 300 roentgens during the first week and an additional 100 roentgens during the first year, and population B received a relatively low dose of 60 roentgens.† On the basis of certain assumptions and calculations (see Appendix, pages 192-4), one may predict that 2 to 3 per cent of population A's first-generation offspring would succumb to lethal genetic events, including miscarriages, stillbirths, neonatal and childhood deaths. This rate would diminish to 1 per cent for the next twenty generations or so, while population B would show less than 0.1 per cent in the first generation and perhaps 0.5 per cent over the next twenty years. Therefore, even in population A, which we assumed to have been exposed to a very substantial dose, the radiation-induced lethal mutations would cause only a slight reduction in reproductive capacity.

If one compares this genetic damage to the reproductive capacity (not to be confused with the somatic damage to the

---

* The selection for various genetic types or "genotypes" is technically referred to as selection for "genetic polymorphism." The full social implications of this genetic concept, particularly in respect to racist theories, have not yet been generally recognized.
† Population A was postulated by Hardin Jones; the 60-roentgen dose received by population B was the Office of Civil and Defense Mobilization's estimate for the average of noninjured survivors in the United States following the 1959 Holifield Hearings attack pattern.

reproductive capacity, which would be very serious indeed) to the normal state of reproductive problems, it becomes apparent that by itself the genetic damage would not lead to any serious impairment of man's ability to reproduce. At the present time, it is estimated that 15 per cent of human pregnancies in North America and Europe terminate in miscarriages or spontaneous abortions, 3 per cent in stillbirths, 2 per cent in neonatal deaths. In addition, deaths among infants after the first month of post-natal life amount to 3 per cent.

In light of the above calculations, the demise of the human population as a result of lethal mutations appears unlikely. Further support for this conclusion is given by geneticists B. Wallace and T. Dobzhansky, who calculate that the reproductive capacity of the descendants of a human population exposed to 400 to 500 roentgens would diminish, but only slightly. However, this "optimistic" conclusion is valid only if the assumptions made are valid. Wallace and Dobzhansky have pointed out that practically nothing is known about the frequencies with which certain lethal mutations arise in man, either spontaneously or as a result of known radiation exposures. One might also question the assumption that the doubling dose is 30 roentgens. The 1962 *Report of the United Nations Scientific Committee on the Effects of Atomic Radiation* states that the 30-roentgen figure is probably valid for men, but that a 15-roentgen figure may prove to be more realistic for the human species in view of the much greater sensitivity of the egg-producing cells of women. The Russian geneticist N. P. Dubinin believes that estimates of the genetic damage in man, based on studies on mice, are unreliable. Dubinin and his coworkers, on the basis of chromosomal aberrations produced in the rhesus monkey and in tissue cultures of human cells, infer that the doubling dose for genetic changes in man is in the neighborhood of 10 roentgens. Other geneticists have suggested that the doubling dose may be around 3 roentgens. If this last estimate proves correct, then the effects discussed above would increase by a factor of 10, which might be very serious for a population that has already suffered substantial somatic incapacitation, including a pronounced reduction in fertility, life shortening, and an increased incidence of degenerative diseases.

Another uncertainty is that the rate of pregnancies that currently terminate as miscarriages and perinatal and early childhood deaths may increase from 23 per cent to a figure close to double that if the surviving population is no longer capable of giving the social and medical care currently provided by modern society. Under such circumstances a tenfold increase in dominant lethals might result in a reduction of reproductive capacity to the point where the only hope of maintaining a population at all would be to outbreed it with a less damaged population.

Other assumptions are also questionable: Is the spontaneous-mutation rate in man one new mutation per ten new gametes? What is the load of lethal mutations currently accumulated? How many more lethals may one add to this burden before jeopardizing biological (in contrast to social) reproductive capacity? At what rate are lethals eliminated in man? Perhaps the assumptions based on fruit-fly studies are not applicable; perhaps lethals are eliminated in a very few generations, thereby increasing the genetic death rate severalfold. Are one-sixth of the mutant genes lethal, or is a higher fraction involved?

The possibility of genetic damage lies not only in lethals but also in nonlethal, but still deleterious, mutations. H. J. Muller has estimated that there are five such harmful mutations for every lethal one. Thus, population A would contain approximately 1,800,000 induced nonlethal mutant genes; population B, approximately 84,000. These detrimental genes would probably be maintained for more than fifty generations. Perhaps 2 per cent of them would show up as obviously defective persons in any one generation—about 30,000 to 40,000 in population A, 1,500 to 2,000 in population B. Although persons with such defects would obviously be handicapped, they would not necessarily be prevented from reproducing. The remaining 98 per cent of the mutant genes would tend to manifest themselves in terms of impaired vigor, fertility, and intelligence. Each descendant of population A would carry on the average of one to two such induced mutations, while in population B about one descendant in twelve would carry such a mutation.

In addition to damage from whole-body radiation from external sources, there is also a threat from fallout contamination of food and water. Radioactive cesium and strontium would increase the radiation dose to the gonads for several generations. Radioactive carbon, with a half life of about 5,800 years, would induce mutations for as long as civilization is old. However, it is unlikely that gonadal irradiation from these sources would exceed the figure of 60 roentgens per generation chosen for population B. Therefore, it seems unlikely that the spontaneous-mutation rate would permanently increase above 1.5 times the current rate. All of the uncertainties discussed earlier also apply to these calculations. As a matter of fact, a recent finding by Swedish scientists indicates that strontium probably replaces calcium in the chromosomes, and that radioactive strontium is highly efficient in producing mutations. Thus, as more information concerning the deleterious effects of fallout radiation accumulates, it may become necessary to revise the above estimates.

The experience of the exposed Japanese populations tends to support the above conclusions. Genetic damage was real but not seriously incapacitating. It expressed itself as a changed sex ratio, one of the most sensitive indicators of genetic damage. Recessive sex-linked lethal mutations caused male progeny to be preferentially eliminated, resulting in more girls than boys born into a damaged population. However, other signs of genetic damage were not observed in Japan. This is not surprising under the circumstances: congenital malformations, for example, would essentially be masked in the first post-bomb generation. But, as indicated above, damage to the genetic information of an irradiated human population scarcely begins to show up during the first generation. Rather, the damage inflicted on future generations would still express itself when, as Wallace and Dobzhansky point out, our present controversies will be mere historic curiosities.

If the genetic damage is likely to perpetuate itself for many generations, so is the cultural damage. And if the *extent* of the genetic damage is a matter of uncertainty, the *extent* of the cultural damage is even more so. Nevertheless, it seems likely that the self-perpetuating cultural damage caused by a nuclear war would be much more incapacitating than the genetic damage. For it would be the psychological legacy which the survivors would pass on to their children and to their children's children which would inhibit the recovery of society.

In his 1957 presidential address to the American Historical Society, William L. Langer clearly showed that great disasters can indeed have long-term psychological repercussions. Focusing particularly on the Black Death of the fourteenth century, he discussed the diverse and long-lasting effects of the wide-scale and sudden population loss, a loss not unsimilar to what may be expected as a result of a nuclear attack. The devastating plague that struck Europe in 1348-9 quickly wiped out a third or even a half of the population in many areas, and it itself was only the beginning of an extended period of pandemic disease which ravaged Europe on and off for about three hundred years.

The social, religious, and economic activities of this period clearly reflect the great impact of the Black Death. The remarkable economic progress of the thirteenth century came to a halt as merchants, clergymen, professors, and anyone else who could fled in terror from the cities. In some places the social chaos and pervading sense of doom made many people turn to immorality and crime, while others, unable to fathom the misery that had so suddenly overcome them, felt it to be an expression of God's wrath and so attempted to appease Him. Penitential exercises— in some cases, flagellant processions—the burning of witches and searching for scapegoats were common. Obsessed with a sense of sin and guilt, and fearing immediate death and damnation, the people turned to magic, astrology, witchcraft, and Satanism. The art of the period reflects their anxiety, depression, and morbid pre-occupation with death—the Dance of Death theme appeared frequently, as did numerous meticulously detailed paintings of Christ's passions, the terrors of the Last Judgment, and the tortures of hell.

Langer cites the German historian Wilhelm Abel, who "holds that pestilence, famine, and war were not enough to account for the enormous decline in population, and that psychological forces, as yet unanalyzed, led to a reluctance to marry and raise a family." Langer himself suggests that a mass emotional disturbance is created when an entire community is struck by a disaster and is subjected to feelings of guilt, demoralization, and helplessness and that "children, having experienced the terror of their parents and the panic of the community, will react to succeeding crises in a similar but even more intense manner. In other words, the anxiety and fear are transmitted from one generation to another, constantly aggravated." This perpetuation of mass fear and hysteria from generation to generation remains somewhat a matter of speculation, but, for whatever reason, the population of England prior to the 1348 plague was approximately 3,700,000 and by

1400 had still not exceeded 2,100,000, and the figures for continental Europe have been estimated to be similar.

E. C. Banfield's study of a poor and backward town in southern Italy, mentioned earlier in Chapter 8, is another case in point. Although no traumatic event precipitated this town's depression, the extreme cultural and economic poverty, combined with a high disease and death rate, have made the villagers suspicious and anxious, and have caused them to pass these attitudes from generation to generation. This sustained demoralization makes co-operation nearly impossible and the townspeople are thus unable to act together for the common good of the community.

Banfield obtained some measure of the villagers' attitudes by administering a number of psychological tests to them. When shown pictures of people in various situations—such as a boy contemplating a violin—and asked to invent stories about them, the vast majority of those tested talked of calamities and misfortunes, of personal neglect and mistreatment, indicating a state of apprehension and fear. Northern Italians shown the violin picture thought the boy was an ambitious lad who wanted to become a violinist, clearly a realistic and "normal" response. In contrast, some of the southern Italians thought the boy was an orphan, others described him as an beggar or a neglected bastard, and one thought he was dying of hunger. In this town, as in much of southern Italy, it appears that ignorance breeds ignorance, distrust breeds distrust, and stagnation perpetuates its misery.

A dramatic example of lingering effects generated by a country-wide disaster is the Great Famine that struck Ireland during the late 1840's. A full century later, the country's population growth, social patterns, and national characteristics still clearly reflect this one traumatic experience.

Prior to the famine, the population of Ireland increased at a rate comparable to, or faster than, the more vigorous European countries. During the eighteenth century and first half of the nineteenth century Ireland's population growth was at least about equal to, or may well have exceeded, that of Great Britain, which was enjoying a period of unprecedented industrial expansion.*

* The Irish increased from an estimated 1,500,000 around 1700 to an estimated 4,000,000 by about 1800. By 1821, one estimate placed the population at 6,800,000, a figure which had increased by another million by 1831. According to more recent estimates, the population was about 5,000,000 in 1780 and increased to 8,000,000 by 1841.

In 1841 the population of Ireland was just over 8,000,000, with an additional 400,000 Irish in Great Britain and other settlements of very substantial size in Canada, Australia, and, of course, the United States. Emigration to the United States between 1840 and 1845 averaged 37,000 persons per year. The marriage rate was high, and Irish men and women married at a comparatively early age, producing thirty babies per year per thousand of the population.

In the early 1840's a blight began attacking the potato crops, first in North America, then in Europe, and then, in the fall of 1845, it struck Ireland more severely than anywhere else. Two scientists were dispatched from England and a commission was set up by the lord lieutenant to suggest means of preserving sound potatoes and possibly utilizing diseased ones. But field after field of potatoes provided fertile ground for the spread of the blight. Just as the scientists failed to understand the nature of the disease, so the government officials did not comprehend its implications for the Irish economy and society. Few anticipated the unfathomable misery that was to descend on Ireland for the next years, although the fact that about one half of the population was dependent on the potato and that even a partial failure of the crop could cause whole families to starve should have been ample warning.

The crop failed completely in 1846, and by the spring and summer of 1847 the famine had caused more than 3,000,000 people to seek public aid. In 1848, the crop again failed completely, and other lean years followed.

Accompanying the famine were not only the obvious diseases of malnutrition such as scurvy and "famine dropsy," but also dysentery, relapsing fever, and typhus. The eyewitness accounts tell of emaciated families huddled together in cottages, dying one by one without food, fuel, or even bedding; of deserted hamlets; of corpses bunched along the roadside; of how Cork, Dublin, and other cities, themselves already overburdened, placed guards at their entrances to prevent the further influx of country paupers.

According to the census of 1851, about 360,000 persons died of epidemic diseases or starvation during the famine years. However, the system of data collection was wholly inadequate so that the number of deaths attributable to the famine probably exceeded

500,000 and may well have reached 1,000,000. These losses, coupled with the heavy emigration, resulted in a 20 per cent decline in population between 1841 and 1851, the rural population showing a 25 per cent decline. The emigration rate jumped to an average of 200,000 persons per year, so that during the decade 1845-55, the Emerald Isle lost over 2,000,000 people to the New World and Australia.

The population of what is now the Irish Republic continued to decline steadily, from around 5,000,000 in the 1850's, to 4,000,000 in the 1870's, to 3,000,000 by 1926; the 1961 census showed the Irish Republic to consist of 2,814,703 persons. This is in marked contrast to other European countries whose populations expanded substantially during this period. Denmark, for example, increased from about 1,500,000 in the 1850's to over 4,500,000 in 1960.

A great part of Ireland's population decline is due to the heavy emigrations which have become almost an Irish way of life. Although the flood of people leaving Ireland following the famine had subsided by the mid-1850's, emigration continued at a rapid rate. In 1865, for example, it involved 100,000 people, and in the twentieth century, about 20,000 people still leave Ireland each year. In fact, a full century after the disaster, Ireland still continued to have the highest emigration rate of any country in the world.

Emigration is only part of the story, however. In addition to maintaining the highest emigration rate in the world for a century, the Irish also maintained the lowest marriage rate, and a hundred years after the famine they still marry later than people of any other nation. It is only because of the traditionally large size of the families that the birth rate has been maintained at levels comparable to those of the United States, although it is still substantially below the pre-famine one.

It might be argued that the perpetuation of the altered social pattern following the famine reflected other pressures on Irish society, such as overpopulation or domination by the English, and that the famine merely acted as a catalyst in bringing about changes that would have occurred and perpetuated themselves anyway. And there is, of course, no way of proving absolutely the contention that one is dealing with sociopsychological forces which were generated by the immense, nationwide disaster. However, a great deal of evidence does indicate that psychological, rather than economic or political, forces are impeding the full recovery of Ireland.

It is generally agreed that, considering the productivity of Ireland in the 1840's, the country was overpopulated. But by the middle of the twentieth century the population density of Ireland is among the lowest to be found in Europe, less than half that of Denmark, Czechoslovakia, Poland, or France, less than a quarter that of Italy, and less than a fifth that of West Germany or the United Kingdom.

It is true that there were outrages committed during the domination of Ireland by the English, but it is doubtful that the Irish fared any worse under the British than did any number of nations in Eastern Europe and the Balkans under the Austrians or Russians. In any case, political freedom has been a fact for over a quarter of a century without appreciably affecting the social pattern of Eire.

On the other hand, studies of Irish oral tradition show how the imprint of the famine has remained in the social culture of the people. Stories of the suffering as the famine struck, of the sight and smell of decay, of the fever, of whole families dying within their cottages, the bodies left to be eaten by rats or hungry dogs because people were too weak or too fearful of catching the fever themselves; stories of hamlets that perished so that only the names of their former sites are remembered—all of these memories have persisted in the folk tales down to this day.

It is clear that the Irish peasantry suffered terribly and that society was shaken to its very roots. Communities in which there had existed a long tradition of communal activities found that doors had become locked. A hospitable people had grown fearful; folk poetry, music, and dancing stopped. "They lost and forgot them all and when the times improved in other respects, these things never returned as they had been. The famine killed everything." And fear lasted. It could be felt in the hushed voices and grim tones of those who could still recall it from the past.

In writing of the emigration during the famine, Oliver Mac-Donagh, Fellow of St. Catharine's College at Cambridge, states that in 1848, which was the year in which the potato crop failed completely for the second time, the failure was accompanied by a collapse in morale. "The mood prevailing from 1848 onwards seems to differ from the earlier terror and excitement. Wherever it is caught, it is marked by a note of doom, an air of finality. . . . This mood explains many of the peculiarities of the famine movement, not least the bitterness and sense of wrong which so many emigrants carried with them to the new world."

Just as Europeans felt the Black Death was an expression of God's anger, many Irishmen believed the famine to be God's punishment for the pre-famine waste of potatoes. This feeling of guilt, combined with the actuality of scarcity, resulted in an attitude of fearful caution and extreme frugality. This attitude was taught to each succeeding generation so that a century later, it was well remembered.*

This sense of frugality continues to permeate Irish life to the extent that it appears to affect the marriage pattern: classified matrimonial advertisements stress the economic assets required of prospective interested parties. Men and women, but particularly men, are reluctant to assume the responsibility of marriage and child rearing. Thus, the majority of Irish emigrants are female, and Eire has the lowest women-to-men ratio of any country in the world.

Undoubtedly the stagnation of Irish society is temporary. Even a cursory examination of the population curves shows that after one hundred years the decline finally has leveled off and that lately there has even been an occasional slight net increase. The famine struck Irish society a grievous blow, but not a fatal one. However, this trauma did reverberate in the minds of Irishmen for at least a century. Still today, Irish commentators call attention to "the racial despair that filled our people during the horror years of the Famine," and author John D. Sheridan, in quoting this observation, points out that "despair of this kind is deeper and more lasting than any personal despair. It is passed on from generation to generation till it becomes a national heritage. The despair of the Famine years . . . left a stain of pessimism on the national character. For we are not, as is commonly supposed, a light-hearted people. We are a little bit afraid of life."

---

* This author's father relates that when he was a boy in Germany, he was taught that "nice" people always left a little food on their plates. To do otherwise would have been considered ill-mannered and greedy. Following the food shortages accompanying World War I, the attitude changed: "nice" little boys now were taught to finish up everything on their plates; otherwise they were charged with being impolite and wasteful.

It is now well understood that a nuclear war would produce a legacy of genetic damage. The fact that survivors would also transmit changes in social information to future generations has received virtually no public attention. Yet such social changes might last as long and have at least as profound an influence on future generations as would the genetic consequences.

We have seen how the effects of great disasters or severe socioeconomic depression may be perpetuated in the culture of a society. There are other examples besides those cited. William L. Langer has suggested that malaria could have been one of the principal factors in the fall of the Etruscan civilization and, to some extent, in the change in character of the Greeks after the fourth century; and the great epidemics of the second and third centuries probably contributed to the tragic fate of the Roman Empire.

But can these examples be applied to a modern industrial nation and to a twentieth-century society's reaction to a nuclear attack? The answer lies implicitly in the fact that a nuclear disaster would be far worse, in both intensity and duration of suffering, than any previously recorded event in human history. We are so intimately involved with, and so inclined to take for granted, our own society that it is difficult to believe that drastic changes can occur. Some people can readily envision post-attack political upheavals like those that racked Europe after World War I— economic and social anarchy followed by the establishment of totalitarian regimes—but to consider a downward spiraling of social organization to a new low not familiar to twentieth-century Western civilization seems to most people almost absurd.

Yet let us summarize for a moment the events likely to be associated with a nuclear assault. In the first place, the attack would kill an unprecedented portion of the nation's population, plus destroying many of its cities, and would leave in its wake an overwhelming number of burned, maimed, or radiation-poisoned injured. In addition, all activity in many nontarget areas would be totally paralyzed because of fallout. The initial critical phase would be followed by severe shortages of the necessities of life and a profound depression of all economic activity, leading to inflation, loss of jobs, and the creation of economic migrants or refugees. An inability to maintain adequate standards of sanitation might lead to epidemics, which would add to the serious somatic debilitation of a radiation-exposed people. A population least able to cope with natural disasters then may be forced to cope with a dislocation of nature not experienced for the last ten millennia: floods, excessively cold weather, insect plagues, dust bowls, erosion, the formation of deserts.

If in their novels Aldous Huxley and Walter Miller have painted extreme pictures of the aftermath of nuclear war, they are no more extreme than some of the so-called objective analysts who believe that a return to prewar society could be achieved within about a decade. These specialists fail to project significantly beyond the experience of the last war. They may be right if nuclear war were restricted to a very limited exchange of detonations, but if the United States were to sustain anything above a few thousand megatons aimed at "population and resources," and if other industrialized countries around the world were subjected to similar assaults, thereby precluding the possibility of relief for America, then such optimistic predictions are based more on fantasy than on realism.

The fate of Mesopotamia is an example of a calamity that destroyed both people and resources. Seven centuries after that war, the population of the area was still less than one third of its prewar figure. A demoralized country neither rebuilds nor recovers rapidly. Instead, social institutions disappear, individual skills are lost, knowledge recedes, and the pall of a dark age descends gloomily on an increasingly ignorant and suspicious people unable to cope with a hostile environment. Such an environment would be created by a nuclear disaster.

EPILOGUE

The many man-made and natural disasters reviewed in this book are not intended as a morbid kaleidoscope of human suffering, but rather are presented in an attempt to evaluate the consequences of a thermonuclear war. It is unlikely that all of the problems discussed in this book would materialize following such a disaster, but, on the other hand, it is quite likely that there would be other problems, which have not even been anticipated here. Nevertheless, the general assessment of conditions following attack is probably not unrealistic.

Why have we made this assessment?

Because no problem can be solved until it is clearly understood.

Nowhere is this truism more applicable than in considering thermonuclear war. Estimates of the effects of nuclear weapons range all the way from the probable destruction of all humanity to the concept that nuclear war differs from conventional warfare only quantitatively and not qualitatively. Each of these assessments has led to different approaches to the problem and to different solutions: If, argues the first side, thermonuclear war is to be prevented at all costs, then any war preparations, including civil-defense precautions, would not only be foolish, they would be clearly immoral.

All efforts should be devoted to achieving world peace. If, counters the other side, the threat of thermonuclear war calls for an expansion of defense, and particularly civil defense, then not making every effort to protect the population would be highly irresponsible and clearly immoral.

After a careful sifting of the information, this study concludes that the consequences of a thermonuclear war are intermediate between the two extreme assessments: Not all people in a country subjected to nuclear assault would die—survival might even be substantial. However, the society of a victim country would be struck such a grievous blow that recovery would be impossible. Furthermore, the suffering inflicted on the contesting populations would surpass anything experienced in recorded history.

For this reason it would be irresponsible and even immoral to rely on World War II techniques for the protection of populations against the ravages of a nuclear war. Following World War I, the French, by building the Maginot Line, helped delude themselves into a false sense of security with an extension of World War I concepts. This magnificent engineering feat not only failed to save France from a determined enemy in World War II, but "Maginot Line psychology" probably contributed substantially to the fall of that unhappy country.

It would be much more sensible for us to admit that current offensive military technology is so able to overwhelm any defenses that a new approach is required. This new approach would seek to avoid attack in the first place by recognizing that national security is assured only in a world in which any and all potential enemies are disarmed. There are several ways this objective might be achieved, but probably the most effective would be to establish a world community in which a stable though divergent society would create a stable peace.

In order to achieve this utopian goal, which would include the creation of new social institutions such as a world legal system, it is first necessary to change certain fundamental social attitudes. This is not nearly as difficult as it is often assumed. Even a cursory examination of the changes in attitudes that have occurred in this country during the twentieth century in regard to the role of women in society, race relations, sex mores, government responsibility for the economic well-being of its citizens, should convince the skeptics of the reality of change. And these shifts in attitudes have not been limited to any one country or any one culture.

Changes in social attitudes involve not only the acquisition of positive new attitudes, such as the sense of belonging to a world community, but also the elimination of certain negative ones, such as the suspicion that anyone who advocates disarmament and peace is either a subversive or a lunatic idealist unable to grasp the realities of today's world.

This book should make it abundantly clear that the quickest way to remove a country from the mainstream of history is to subject it to thermonuclear attack. No nation is exempt. Nonindustrialized countries could not cope with the medical and ecological problems created by fallout. Industrialized countries could not survive the destruction of the cities. Society would collapse in either case. For this reason, a preoccupation with peace is not only eminently reasonable and respectable, but in our generation has become imperative.

APPENDICES

APPENDIX TO CHAPTER 3

Broido and McMasters in their extensive report *Effects of Mass Fires on Personnel in Shelters* (1960) review much pertinent information, as well as report the results of their several experimental fires. In respect to carbon monoxide poisoning they cite the work of Claudy in terms of the following table (p. 25):

TABLE 1

Effects of Carbon Monoxide

CARBON MONOXIDE CONTENT OF INHALED AIR (PER CENT)	EFFECTS
0.02	Possible mild frontal headache after 2 to 3 hours.
0.04	Frontal headache and nausea after 1 to 2 hours. Occipital (rear of head) headache after 2½ to 3½ hours.
0.08	Headache, dizziness, and nausea in ¾ hour. Collapse and possible unconsciousness in 2 hours.

Effects of Carbon Monoxide

CARBON MONOXIDE CONTENT OF INHALED AIR (PER CENT)	EFFECTS
0.16	Headache, dizziness, and nausea in 20 minutes. Collapse, unconsciousness, and possible death in 2 hours.
0.32	Headache and dizziness in 5 to 10 minutes. Unconsciousness and danger of death in 30 minutes.
0.64	Headache and dizziness in 1 to 2 minutes. Unconsciousness and danger of death in 10 to 15 minutes.
1.28	Immediate effect. Unconsciousness and danger of death in 1 to 3 minutes.

On the basis of information compiled by Sollman, Broido and McMasters provide the following tables (p. 24):

TABLE 2

Effects of Oxygen Deficiency

OXYGEN CONTENT OF INHALED AIR (PER CENT)	EFFECTS
20.9	No effects; normal air.
15.0	No immediate effects.
10.0	Dizziness, shortness of breath, deeper and more rapid respiration, quickened pulse, especially on exertion.
7.0	Stupor sets in.
5.0	Minimal concentration compatible with life.
2-3.0	Death within one minute.

TABLE 3
Effects of Carbon Dioxide (oxygen content normal)

CARBON DIOXIDE CONTENT OF INHALED AIR (PER CENT)	EFFECTS
.04	No effects; normal air.
2.0	Breathing deeper, tidal volume increased 30%.
4.0	Breathing much deeper, rate slightly quickened, considerable discomfort.
4.5-5.0	Breathing extremely labored, almost unbearable for many individuals. Nausea may occur.
7-9.0	Limit of tolerance.
10-11.0	Inability to co-ordinate; unconsciousness in about 10 minutes.
15-20.0	Symptoms increase, but probably not fatal in 1 hour.
25-30.0	Diminished respiration, fall of blood pressure, coma, loss of reflexes, anesthesia. Gradual death after some hours.

Estimate of Extent of Fire Hazard

In the absence of sufficient data on fire initiation by megaton-class weapons, any prediction of fire-damage areas becomes tenuous. Broido, in his article "Mass Fires Following Nuclear Attack" (1960), indicates that a ten-megaton weapon could produce heat ignition out to distances greater than 35 miles (p. 411). *Effects of Nuclear Weapons* (1957) indicates that one may expect the ignition of fire-kindling fuels to occur at a distance of 30 miles for a twenty-megaton air burst (p. 508). *Medical Effects of the Atomic Bomb in Japan* (1956) indicates that at Hiroshima the firestorm eventually covered a circular area of about 4.5 miles (p. 17). This involves a radius of about 1.2 miles. Similarly, in Nagasaki, where no firestorm developed, all buildings within about 1.25 miles of ground zero were destroyed by flames (ENW, p. 326). The Hiroshima bomb had a yield of about twenty kilotons, the Nagasaki bomb was somewhat more powerful (MEJ, p. 11). The Hiroshima bomb was exploded at about 1,800 feet (MEJ, p. 17), so that 1.2

miles from ground zero would involve a slant range of 1.25 miles. At this distance a twenty-megaton bomb would deliver about 12 cal/sq cm (ENW, pp. 338-9). Providing atmospheric conditions are favorable, a twenty-megaton low air burst could deliver this amount of energy at 28 miles from the explosion (ENW, p. 306). This amount of energy is delivered over a much longer period of time with the twenty-megaton weapon; hence it would be only about half as effective as the Hiroshima bomb (ENW, pp. 298, 332-3). Furthermore, the development of a firestorm seems to be more related to the density of combustible material than to the area in which fires are started. Nevertheless, it is conceivable that late in the summer or fall, on an exceptionally clear day, following a dry spell, the presence of dry fallen leaves (ENW, p. 308) would insure that many fires would be readily started and that there would be a continuum of combustible material. Under these circumstances, mass fires would occur out to 28 miles from the detonation (12 cal/sq cm).

Because a megaton-class weapon delivers its energy more slowly (ENW, pp. 298, 332-3), and because of atmospheric attenuation (ENW, p. 335-6), a 30 cal/sq cm line would appear to be more probable as delineating the area of fire initiation. This amount of energy would be delivered on a clear day out to 18 miles from a low air burst (ENW, p. 339). For a contact surface burst, the above distances would have to be reduced by 40 per cent (ENW, p. 298).

TABLE 4 *

Population Density and Area: New York City (1960 census) vs. Center of Hiroshima

	PERSONS PER SQ. MILE	AREA
Manhattan	75,072	22.6
Brooklyn	33,446	78.5
Bronx	33,032	43.1
Queens	15,777	114.7
Staten Island	3,648	60.9
Hiroshima Center (as of August 1, 1945)	25,000	4.0

* Extrapolated from Office of Civil and Defense Mobilization, *Fire Effects of Bombing Attacks* (1955), p. 18.

APPENDIX TO CHAPTER 5

Medical Aspects of Radiation Injury

According to the government report *The Effects of Ionizing Radiation on Human Beings* (1956), individuals exposed to radiation doses in the vicinity of the LD50, in which survival is possible, show the following changes in the hemopoietic tissues: Lymphocytes are profoundly depressed within hours and remain so for months. The neutrophile count is depressed to low levels, the degree and time of maximum depression depending upon the dose. Signs of infection may be seen after 7 to 9 days, when the total neutrophile count has dropped virtually to zero. The platelet count may reach very low levels after 2 weeks. External evidence of bleeding may occur within 2 or 4 weeks. This group represents the lethal dose range in the classical pharmacologic sense. In the higher-exposure groups of this category, the latent period lasts from 1 to 3 weeks with little clinical evidence of injuries other than slight fatigue. At the termination of the latent period, the patient may develop purpura, epilation, oral and cutaneous lesions, infections of wounds or burns, diarrhea, and melena.

Among those for whom survival is improbable and among those for whom it is possible, the blood picture is not as well documented as it is for those whose prognosis is more hopeful. There are good clinical reasons to believe that in the lethal range the granulocyte depressions will be marked and below 1,000 per mm^3 during the second week. Good observations in Japan confirm this contention. However, in the sublethal range it takes much longer for the granulocyte count and platelet count of man to reach minimal values, as compared to other mammals. The granulocytes may show some depression during the 2nd and 3rd week. However, there can be considerable variation. A late fall in the granulocytes during the 6th or 7th week may occur and should be watched for. Platelet counts reach the lowest level on approximately the 30th day; at this time maximum bleeding was observed in Japanese who were exposed at Hiroshima and Nagasaki. This time trend in the platelet count and the development of hemorrhage is in marked contrast to what was observed in laboratory animals, in which platelets reach their lowest level around the 10th to 15th day and hemorrhage occurs shortly thereafter. Among those for whom survival is probable, individuals with neutrophile counts below 1,000/mm^3 or less may show no external signs of bleeding.

Problems in Predicting the Fallout Pattern

One assumes a "ground-zero circle," which includes the fallout of heavier particles from the initial column and mushroom cloud. This material descends within the first hour after detonation. The lighter particles take a longer time to come down and are displaced horizontally by wind. The ground-zero circle thus is displaced downwind, forming first an ellipse, and ultimately a cigar-shaped figure. Baum, testifying before the June 1959 Holifield Hearings on Biological and Environmental Effects of Nuclear War, reported that the best available estimate of the range of significant sizes in areas of hazardous fallout is 50 to 400 microns (μ) (p. 189). It takes a 340μ particle ¾ hour to descend from 80,000 feet, and a 75μ particle 16 hours. According to *Effects of Nuclear Weapons* (1957), with a 15-mph wind the 340μ particle would be blown about 8 miles from ground zero, the 75μ particle about 220 miles (pp. 440-1). With a 15-knot wind, the lighter particles tend to arrive almost horizontally: a 300μ particle at an 18½° angle from the horizontal, a 30μ particle at a ½° angle (Hawkins, in Holifield, p. 169).

Given the data in ENW (pp. 417-21), in the idealized pattern of fallout descent it is possible to plot the dose-rate contours. Shelton estimated that a ten-megaton weapon would contaminate an area of about 2,500 square miles to the extent that an unshielded person at the edge of this area would receive 450 rem in 48 hours (Holifield, p. 41). This assumed a 15-knot wind producing a pattern 150 miles long downwind, and 25 miles at its widest. It was also assumed that the radioactive decay rate of the deposited material followed the $t^{-1.2}$ rate (Holifield, p. 46; ENW, p. 432).

Unfortunately, almost every assumption that needs to be made in the above type of calculation is uncertain. Machta points out that the smooth simplified contours described are produced by simplified wind structures, and these often do not exist (Holifield, pp. 130, 136). At several altitudes winds may show varying velocities and varying directions. Thus a five-megaton burst of the 1956 REDWING series in the Pacific produced a pattern resembling an ameba. Triffet indicates that in that instance, the ground-zero circle could be approximated at one hour after the explosion by a 1,000-roentgens-per-hour (r/hr) contour. Almost 50 miles away there were two hot spots exceeding 2,500 r/hr, and one of these was close enough to the edge so that the 25 r/hr contour was within 20 miles of the hot spot (Holifield, p. 80).

The $t^{-1.2}$ law has also proved to be in error. According to new data obtained by the Naval Radiological Defense Laboratory, the radioactive decay rate deviates considerably from the average rate usually estimated ($\propto t^{-1.2}$)—being slower at earlier times and faster at later times (Holifield, p. 100). The newer data indicate that at one hour after detonation there would be a dose rate 2.3 times higher than that anticipated from the $t^{-1.2}$ decay rate. After several months the two curves intersect, and 6 months or later the anticipated radiation doses are less than those calculated on the basis of the $t^{-1.2}$ law (pp. 77, 125). A third estimate was arrived at by Lapp on the basis of data obtained from Kabelle and Gejen Islands contaminated by the March 1954 BRAVO test (pp. 218-23). The immediate (first-hour) decay follows the $t^{-1.2}$ rule, but is followed by a $t^{-1.3}$ relation which is assumed to be valid until 3 weeks. From 3 weeks to 6 months, a $t^{-1.5}$ relation holds, at the end of which time a $t^{-2.2}$ rate describes the decay more accurately. This means that at 6 months the radiation is an order of magnitude lower than the theoretical value given by *Effects of Nuclear Weapons* (this has been corrected in the new, 1962 edition of ENW, p. 420); and at 5 years the divergence between the two curves amounts to a factor of 100 (Holifield, p. 219).

There are several reasons why the decay rate differs from the theoretical one: the shape of the fission yield curves in U235 and U238 is different and the shape of the fast-fission curve differs markedly from that for slow fission. Ruthenium 106 and antimony 125 are unimportant for U235 but become significant for fast U238 fission (Lapp, in Holifield, p. 211).

Another uncertainty is created by a process known as fractionation; that is, not all radioisotopes settle out of the atmosphere with equal rapidity. For example, most of the strontium 90 produced by the bomb derives from the noble gas krypton $Kr90 \xrightarrow{33 \text{ sec}} Rb90 \xrightarrow{2.7 \text{ min}} Sr90$. Because of this volatile ancestry, Sr90 is formed as finely divided particles, some of which are so small that they may remain suspended in the earth's atmosphere for years (E. A. Martell, in *Science,* Vol. 129, pp. 1197-1206). Lapp and Triffet point out that the gamma emitter cesium 137 is similarly depleted from the local fallout (Holifield, pp. 72, 74, 217). Lapp states that analysis of a sample obtained from Biijiri-Rojoa sand about a week after the Mike-megaton shot early in November 1952 indicated that whereas the sample was depleted in Cs137, it was enriched in Co60 (p. 221).

Machta has questioned the assumption that 80 per cent of the radioactive material produced will return to earth as local fallout (Holifield, p. 139). It might be much less; for example, the 1962 edition of *Effects of Nuclear Weapons* assumes 60 per cent will descend locally (p. 437). On the other hand, the fallout resulting from a city surface burst on granite might possess quite different properties from those studied thus far. First, the size of the particles would show a different distribution. Triffet points out that large amounts of iron, which would condense early in the cloud, would influence particle formation and rate of descent (Holifield, pp. 64, 70, 72). Second, it is difficult to assess the contribution made to the residual radiation by the neutron-induced activity of such structural materials as steel, glass, and concrete, containing sodium, silicon, iron, copper, zinc, manganese, and cobalt (ENW, pp. 398-9; ENW 1962, pp. 433-4; Holifield, pp. 93, 221). For example, both cobalt and nickel may give rise to radioisotopes of cobalt (Co60, Co58) which, as Strom et al. point out, could constitute a considerable portion of the gamma fallout hazard, particularly at times greater than one year (*Science,* Vol. 128, pp. 417-19).

It is not clear how much of the total radioactive material created by the bomb would remain in the ground-zero circle. In addition to the material vaporized by the bomb and subsequently returned as fallout, there would be a fair amount of material that would not be vaporized but would be subjected to a sufficiently high neutron flux from the initial nuclear radiation to become radioactive. Part of this would comprise the throwout (ENW, p. 60), the rest would remain in the area surrounding the crater (ENW, p. 409; Triffet, in Holifield, p. 103). The deposition of the ground-zero-circle fallout would undoubtedly be modified by the updraft of the firestorm (Hawkins, Ham, in Holifield, pp. 170-1, 240; Broido and McMasters, 1959), although the firestorm is not thought to influence the over-all pattern (Machta, in Holifield, p. 127).

Baum states that not only may the firestorm modify the deposition of fallout locally, but micrometeorological and terrain factors such as wind structures in built-up communities also would cause the fallout to be deposited in a manner far different from the deposition on a flat plane. Although extrapolations cannot be performed with confidence, it is probable that the over-all effects of terrain and weather reduce the hazard predicted on the basis of current assumptions (Holifield, pp. 187-9).

Fallout Estimate for Twenty-Megaton Columbus Circle Burst

Winds in the deep column of the atmosphere (0 to 60,000 feet) around New York on October 17, 1958 (the day of the 1959 Holifield Hearings' assumed attack) were west southwest with an average velocity of 40 mph (Holifield, pp. 44-5). Under these circumstances, the fallout would be blown over Long Island, southern Connecticut, Rhode Island, and Massachusetts, including Cape Cod. If one uses Shelton's estimate, one would expect an area of the order of 5,000 square miles as being delimited by the 450 rem during the first 48 hours contour (p. 41). The 450-rem figure is assumed to be the LD50 (p. 31). For reasons indicated below, this estimate should be revised as follows.

Lapp assumes local fallout to be a field uniformly contaminated to a level of 2 kilotons of fission products per square mile (2 KT/ sq mi). Such a level would be achieved by a twenty-megaton (50 per cent fission) bomb depositing locally 8 megatons of fission products over 4,000 square miles (Holifield, p. 216). Should only 30 per cent of the fallout be deposited locally, instead of the assumed 80 per cent, then the 2 KT/sq mi fallout field would cover 1,500, not 4,000, square miles. Alternatively, one could assume that the fallout field might cover 4,000 square miles, but under these circumstances only to an average level of 0.75 KT/sq mi. In that case, the figures given in the tables below would have to be reduced to 37.5 per cent of the given value. Similarly, should the fission yield of the weapon be only about 5 per cent, instead of the assumed 50-50 yield, then the figures given below would have to be reduced by a factor of 10.

With these qualifications (as well as the others) in mind, one may calculate dose rates for the 4,000-square-mile fallout field contaminated to a level of 2 KT/sq mi as follows: *Effects of Nuclear Weapons* indicates the 2 kilotons involve 3½ ounces of fission products, with an activity of 600 megacuries (pp. 391, 435). At three feet above ground this might produce 600 x 4 r/hr = 2,400 r/hr, providing, as ENW considered reasonable, that the gamma rays have energies of approximately 0.7 Mev (pp. 435, 436). Lapp questions these figures and, citing data of Bolles and Ballou, calculates that the 2-kiloton fission products would yield 940, not 600, megacuries, and that the average energy is 0.92 Mev per photon, and 1.2 photons per disintegration. From these data he calculates the radiation dose rate to be 7,000 r/hr (Holifield, p. 216). He concludes that the 2,400 r/hr value given by ENW is the lower limit, the 7,000 r/hr, the upper limit, of radiation dose one hour after detonation (pp. 216-17). On the basis of actual field data, he uses a 4,000 r/hr rate as a realistic radiation dose (p. 220). Actually, figures published subsequent to Lapp's calculations indicate that for a 2 KT/sq mi fallout field, 5,500 r/hr is more realistic (Holifield Civil Defense Hearings, 1960, p. 563). Moreland gives the following formula for calculating radiation dose rates from weapon debris:

$$\text{Dose rate from megaton weapon} = 2,750 \ t^{-1.23} \ \frac{\text{r/hr}}{\text{KT/sq mi}}$$

where t is measured in hours.

For times up to 100 days the relation is accurate to within 25 per cent. For times greater than 100 days the power law approximation overestimates the dose rate by as much as a factor of 9.

Moreland also provides a schedule of dose rates given a fallout field of 1 KT/sq mi (Holifield C. D., 1960, p. 570). The following table has been converted to 2 KT/sq mi:

TABLE 1

Dose Rates for Local Fallout

TIME	DOSE (IN ROENTGENS)	TIME	DOSE (IN ROENTGENS)
1st - 6th hours	7,810	1st month	18,200
6th-12th "	2,090	2nd month	936
12th-24th "	2,200	3rd "	412
1st day	12,100	4th "	248
2nd day	1,650	5th "	170
3rd "	550	6th "	138
4th "	440	7th "	82
5th "	276	8th "	82
6th "	276	9th "	66
7th "	276	10th "	38
1st week	16,120	11th "	38
		12th "	28
2nd week	1,046	1st year	20,460
3rd "	622		
4th "	490	2nd year	88
5th "	298	3rd "	22
6th "	214	4th "	16.6
7th "	182	5th "	13.8

By simple addition one would obtain the following approximate figures for the maximum dose rates received from fallout in a 2 KT/sq mi field:

TABLE 2

Maximum Dose Rates Expected in a 2 KT/sq mi Fallout Field
(in roentgens)

From the end of the	1st hour	to the end of the	2nd day	= 14,000
From " " " "	2nd day	" " " " "	2nd week	= 3,000
From " " " "	2nd week	" " " " "	2nd month	= 2,000
From " " " "	2nd month	" " " " "	1st year	= 1,300

In evaluating these figures in terms of the actual radiological hazard involved, at least two corrections need to be made. First, the 14,000 r figure for the period t + 1 hr to t + 48 hr is too high because it assumes that all the fallout is down during the first hour. *The Probable Fallout Threat Over the Continental United States* (1960), a report prepared by Callahan et al., indicates that in respect to radioactivity, the median particle size is 150μ (pp. 97-8); on p. 106, by extrapolations from Fig. 4.3, it would appear that the mean pressure altitude for a twenty-megaton mushroom cloud is 75,000 feet. The descent time for a 150μ particle from this altitude is indicated by these authors to be about 7 hours (p. 102). If one considers the theoretical total integrated dose received at a point three feet above a contaminated (smooth and infinite) plane assuming all the fallout down at t + 1 hr (as in Table 2), then the following is true: about 60 per cent of the total dose received between t + 1 hr and t + 48 hr will be received by t + 7 hr (Holifield C. D., 1960, p. 568). However, the median particle descending from the mean altitude of a twenty-megaton mushroom cloud does not reach the ground until about seven hours after detonation. Hence, roughly 60 per cent of the t + 1 hr to t + 48 hr dose may be ignored in calculating average dose rates of the hypothetical fallout field. A factor of 0.4 is also given by Callahan et al. to compensate for the descent time (p. 198). Thus the 14,000 r figure should be reduced to 5,600 r. However, the dose will be considerably higher nearer to ground zero where the heavier particles descend earlier; at greater downwind distances, the lighter particles will be deposited much later, causing the dose to be less

A second correction stems from the fact that the doses in Table 2 are calculated for a point three feet above a uniformly contaminated, hard, flat plane, and have not been corrected for drifting, shielding, and weathering. Knapp, testifying at the 1960 Holifield Civil Defense Hearings, estimated an over-all protection factor which increases from about 1.3 in the first month to about 3 after the first month, then increases to about 4 by the end of two years (p. 577).

In view of these considerations the following is more likely to describe the actual dose rates received by unshielded objects exposed to a 2 KT/sq mi fallout field:

TABLE 3

Probable Dose Rates Expected in a 2 KT/sq mi Fallout Field (in roentgens)

From the end of the 1st hour	to the end of the 2nd day	= 5,600
From " " " " 2nd day	" " " " " 2nd week	= 2,300
From " " " " 2nd week	" " " " " 2nd month	= 670
From " " " " 2nd month	" " " " " 1st year	= 430

According to Lapp, the variations in the levels of fallout within the fallout field would be at least tenfold (Holifield, p, 216). Judging from the five-megaton REDWING shot, Triffet indicates that the variation could well be greater than that (p. 80). Thus, it would appear possible that hot spots of over 50,000 r/48 hr would be encountered on the one hand and doses of 500 r/48 hr or less toward the edge of this hypothetical, 4,000-square-mile, fallout field on the other (see also testimony of Shafer, in Holifield, p. 191). Lapp states that these hot spots are likely to be of the order of 75 miles downwind from ground zero (p. 225). This means that such a hot spot might be observed in the Long Island Sound off Southhold.

In general, the above estimates probably exaggerate the radiological hazard from the New York burst. Not only may the local fallout be much less than 80 per cent, and the fission yield much lower than 50 per cent, but high wind velocities are likely to dilute the field appreciably and deposit much of the radioactivity in the Long Island Sound and the Atlantic Ocean. Long Island is about 120 miles long. If a 150µ particle takes about 7 hours to descend from 75,000 feet, a 40-mph wind could displace such a particle up to 280 miles from ground zero. According to Callahan et al., the mean integrated wind speeds at 80,000 feet over Hempstead during winter, spring, summer, and fall are 43, 29, 14, and 29 knots respectively (1 knot = 1.15 mph) (pp. 78-81). Assuming a 33-mph (about 29 knots) wind, the median fallout particle (150µ) descending from the mean pressure altitude (75,000 feet) will land over 200 miles downwind. Only particles that descend within about four hours will land on Long Island. From 75,000 feet this involves particles larger than 200µ, which means that about 60 per cent of the total radioactivity, carried on smaller particles, will be blown beyond Long Island (Callahan et al., pp. 98, 102).

In addition to the 60 per cent blown farther out, another 10 per cent or so might drop in the blast area itself. Callahan et al. cite the RAND Corporation's Report No. 309, which indicates that as much as 10 per cent of the total radioactivity resides in the stem of the mushroom cloud (p. 101). The stem contains the heaviest particles dug out of the ground, which descend very rapidly and close to ground zero.

For these reasons it seems likely that Long Island would receive only 30 per cent of the anticipated 8 megatons of fission products, or 2.4 megatons. If the fallout field were about 40 miles wide and 120 miles long, then the 2.4 megatons would be distributed over a 4,800-square-mile area. This amounts to about 0.5 KT/sq mi, roughly one fourth of what has been assumed. However, all of this material would have descended within four hours so that the $t + 1$ hr to $t + 48$ hr figure should only be reduced by a factor of about 0.375, while the other figures should be reduced by a factor of 0.25. It must be understood that these corrections apply only in the presence of a 33-mph wind, and that they assume that both particle size and particle behavior will be as described on the basis of previous test shots.

TABLE 4

*Average Dose Rates in a 4,800-Square-Mile Fallout Field
Following a Twenty-Megaton Surface Burst (in Roentgens)*

(Assuming 50 Per Cent Fission Yield, 80 Per Cent Local Fallout,
and Wind Velocity of 29 Knots)

From the end of the 1st hour	to the end of the 2nd day	=	2,100
From " " " " 2nd day	" " " " " 2nd week	=	575
From " " " " 2nd week	" " " " " 2nd month	=	170
From " " " " 2nd month	" " " " " 1st year	=	100

As such, the estimate in Table 4 is probably on the low side,
since only 30 per cent of the fallout would be expected to descend
on the hypothetical 4,800-square-mile fallout field produced by the
single twenty-megaton New York ground burst. Moreover, a fallout
field produced by two or more detonations at different sites would
show substantially high levels of radiation, not so much initially,
when the radiation from the nearest burst would predominate, but
after a few days, as the radioactivity of the closer burst decayed.
For this reason, Table 3 (2 KT/ sq mi) represents a more probable
dose estimate.

APPENDIX TO CHAPTER 7

Fallout Contamination of Surface Water Supplies

One may calculate the contamination of water stored in an
open reservoir 200 feet in diameter with a capacity of about
3,000,000 gallons as follows. Such a reservoir would present a
surface of almost 3 acres; if one assumes the fallout to deposit 640
megacuries of fission products per square mile (about 2 KT/sq
mi, see Appendix to Chapter 5, p, 182), the reservoir would re-

ceive the equivalent of 3 megacuries at one hour after detonation (640 acres/sq mi). This means about 1 curie (C) per gallon, or about 250 millicuries (mC) per liter. According to Hawkins (1960), it is highly probable that at least 90 per cent of the radioactivity will be tied up in an insoluble form (p. 21). *Effects of Nuclear Weapons* (1957) considers that for an emergency consumption period of 10 days, 0.09 mC/liter is acceptable; for a 30-day period, 0.03 mC/liter is acceptable (p. 535). According to the 1960 Holifield Civil Defense Hearings, if the alpha and beta decay parallels that of the gamma emitters, then the acceptable level of 0.09 mC/liter would be achieved in about 5 days and the 0.03 mC/liter level in about 12 days.

Again, these figures are extremely tentative. Atomic shots set off from towers in Nevada produced particles in which less than 2 per cent of the radioactivity was water soluble. However, balloon shots at Nevada produced fallout in which 31 per cent of the radioactivity of the larger particles, and 14 per cent of the radioactivity of the smaller particles (i.e., those less than 44 microns in diameter, was soluble (Holifield Fallout Hearings, p. 2008).

Strontium 90 Contamination of Foodstuffs Grown in Fallout Field Subjected to 1 KT/sq mi

In reference to Lapp's suggestion (see p. 81), the following calculations are pertinent: 10 megatons of fission produce 1,000,000 curies of Sr90 (in Holifield, Fallout Hearings, pp. 1971, 1978, 2427). One kiloton per square mile (1 KT/sq mi) would mean a contamination rate of 100 C/sq mi. Using the formula of Kulp and Schulert (1962, p. 632); that is, that by direct absorption of the fallout into the forage crops, milk calcium levels will average to about 0.65 μμC Sr90/gm Ca/mC per sq mi, one can calculate the 1 KT/sq mi field to result in milk contamination of 65,000 μμC Sr90/gm Ca. The discrimination exercised by the human body against strontium in the Western diet amounts to a factor of 4 (Kulp and Schulert, p. 620). Therefore, newly forming bone would attain a level of about 16,000 μμC Sr90/gm Ca. This is eight times the 2,000 μμC Sr90/gm Ca, acceptable to a high-risk industrial population, that Lapp referred to. For adults, on the other hand, the concentration would approximate the 2,000 μμC

Sr90/gm Ca level since adult bone concentrates about one eighth the amount infants do. In the United States in 1960, the infant level was at 3.3 μμC Sr90/gm Ca, the adult level at 0.4 μμC Sr90/gm Ca; i.e., about 5,000 less than the projected concentration (Kulp and Schulert, p. 626).

APPENDIX TO CHAPTER 10

Theoretical Considerations of the Biological Basis of the Long-Term Somatic Effects

The diverse radiation effects observed may well relate to one primary mechanism. In view of the various hypotheses it may be somewhat arbitrary to single out any one; however, a working hypothesis based principally on one proposed by Puck et al. (1957) is of sufficient cogency to warrant re-emphasis, if for no other reason than that it is immensely helpful in integrating the diverse and often puzzling observations.*

The growth of the mammalian body is generally considered to be determinate; that is, the animal grows to a certain definite size and then stops. However, this is only a partial description, for most tissues continue their growth, although there is no net increase in size; that is, there is a continuing turnover of cells. This turnover is greatest in tissue in which cells are continuously destroyed and sloughed off, as in the epithelium lining the intestines. In stable organs, the turnover is very low. Presumably, there is no cell turnover in the mature nervous system, although newly synthesized protoplasm appears to stream continuously down the axon (see P. Weiss, "The Life History of the Neuron," *Journal of Chronic Diseases* [1956], pp. 340-8). Puck considers the primary effect of radiation to be the chromosomal damage incurred by a

* For a stimulating discussion of various hypotheses proposed to explain how radiation exerts its deleterious effects, see Bernard L. Strehler, "Origin and Comparison of the Effects of Time and High-Energy Radiations on Living Systems," *Quarterly Review of Biology*, Vol. 34 (1959), pp. 117-42.

hit cell which results in that cell losing the capacity to proliferate indefinitely. Cells not in an active state of division are not affected at all until they are stimulated into division. At such a time they simply fail to divide (or possibly, some may perish). Much of the radiation damage remains latent. Therefore, the primary effect of radiation involves the incapacitation of the cells' proliferative ability causing a reduction, potential or actual, of the normal turnover rate in the adult body, and an upset in the normal morphogenetic events in the embryo. On this basis, almost all the observations discussed in Chapter 10, except the carcinogenic effect, become explicable. The impaired ability to repair any organ or part of the body that is challenged is self-evident, since such repair entails cell replacement.

Not too different is the explanation for the reduction in life span and the advanced aging phenomenon. The aging process in itself involves a slowing down of cellular turnover. This is manifested in the difficulties observed in wound repair in older persons as well as the difficulties aging organisms encounter in coping with even minor insults. The superimposing of a cell population made impotent by radiation on a system already encountering difficulty in its normal turnover rates would clearly aggravate degenerative processes. The impaired-turnover concept would explain the inability to maintain a healthy vascular system, which is the basis for a number of degenerative diseases. Thus, the net effect is one of acceleration of aging. This would also explain why an older or less vigorous population would be more susceptible, or why a previous radiation dose (resulting in a certain percentage of incapacitated cells) generally increases the sensitivity to a second radiation dose.

If, in addition to mere replacement, the proliferative capacity of cells is required for the normal growth processes of immature organs or systems, the deleterious impact of radiation is even more severe. During mammalian embryogenesis, the successive morphogenetic events are on an extremely strict and inflexible timetable. If a tissue fails to form, or forms only incompletely, it almost never gets a chance to make up the missing portion. In view of the sensitivity of embryonic neural tissue to radiation, it is not surprising that sublethal doses result in microcephaly, or that radiation of the epiphysis results in the reduced growth of the affected bone. Similarly, it is not surprising that irradiating the cells of the eye's anterior epithelium should lead to the formation of abnormal lens tissue. Nor is it unexpected in view of the above concepts that irradiating the gametogenic epithelia results in reduced fertility. The increased sensitivity of fetuses and children to radiation is consistent with the above postulates.

Probably the normal homeostatic mechanisms of the body compensate for the radiation-damaged cells by causing the proliferation of other cells not incapacitated (though perhaps otherwise altered) by the radiation. These cells are therefore stimulated into division rates exceeding those normally encountered. This process may also be related to the carcinogenic effect of radiation. That is, irrespective of the primary mechanism by which radiation induces a cancer cell, the humoral factors acting upon an irradiated tissue may tend to select for a potentially autonomous cell. Thus, the appearance of tumors as a result of exposure to high doses of radiation (which are not completely destructive) may involve two independent and distinct mechanisms.

APPENDIX TO CHAPTER 13

In order to calculate the genetic damage caused by increasing exposure to ionizing radiation, it is first necessary to establish (1) the spontaneous mutation rate and (2) the radiation dose required to double this spontaneous mutation rate. W. L. Russell and E. M. Kelly (1958) provide the following data on radiation-induced mutation rate in mice. In spermatogonia the rate is $21 \times 10^{-8}/r/$gene for acute exposures and $5 \times 10^{-8}/r/$gene for chronic exposures (10 r/week or 90 r/week). In oöcytes the corresponding rates are $31 \times 10^{-8}/r/$gene for acute, and $4 \times 10^{-8}/r/$gene for chronic irradiation. Mature sperms show a higher rate of $45 \times 10^{-8}/r/$gene, which is independent of dose-rate variations since it is manifest following either acute or chronic irradiation. The spontaneous mutation rate in both males and females is $7 \times 10^{-6}/$gene.

The question arises, does such mouse data have applicability

to human mutation rates? Grahn feels that "Our present thinking is that the sensitivity of man is probably very close to that
of the mouse, based on volume of genetic material involved. We
have reasons to believe that the mouse mutation rates can be
applied to man and be accurate at least within a factor of about
two" (Grahn, 1960, p. 77).

If this is so, then one could make the following calculations. For
acute radiation, the radiation-induced mutation rate is of the
order of 25 x 10^{-8}/r/gene for spermatogonia and oöcytes. This
would mean 750 x 10^{-8}/30 r/gene or 7.5 x 10^{-6}/30 r/gene to approximate the spontaneous mutation rate of 7 x 10^{-6}/gene. Thus,
the doubling dose required to achieve doubling of the spontaneous
mutation rate is of the order of 30 roentgens for an acute dose.
The chronic dose is only a fourth to a fifth as effective as the
acute dose. Thus the doubling dose is in the neighborhood of 120
roentgens for chronic irradiation (UN, 1962, ¶ 154, p. 101).

The 300-roentgens acute dose to which population A is exposed
(see Chapter 13, p. 156) is equivalent to ten times the doubling
dose. The additional 100-roentgens chronic dose is perhaps another 80 per cent of the doubling dose. Thus, population A is
exposed to a dose which would induce a mutation rate 10.8
times over and above the spontaneous mutation rate for man.
Population B, on the other hand, would receive a dose which is
approximately one half the doubling dose, so that in population
B one would expect only a 50 per cent increase in mutation rates.

The question is, what does a 50 per cent rise, or a tenfold increase, in mutation rate signify? Muller (1957) has calculated
that the spontaneous mutation rate is 1 x 10^{-1} per human gamete,
and that the accumulated load of lethal mutations, carried hetero-
zygously, amounts to about 8 per individual. In population A the
mutation rate would then increase by 1.08 genes/gamete or 2.16
genes/individual; that is, on the average, each gamete would
acquire in excess of one new mutation as a result of exposure, and
each individual derived from such gametes would carry in excess
of two such induced mutations. In population B, the mutation
rate would increase from 1 x 10^{-1} to 1.5 x 10^{-1}/gamete, or to
3 x 10^{-1}/individual.

Assume that both hypothetical populations A and B contain
1,000,000 individuals under 40 years of age each, and that one
is dealing with static populations; i.e., each generation produces

exactly 1,000,000 individuals to replace it. Then population A will contain 2,160,000 induced mutant genes, while B will contain 100,000.

Muller (1957) states that in *Drosophila* the average lethal mutation in an autosome might be expected to persist for some 22 generations; detrimental (in contrast to lethal) mutations can be expected to persist in excess of 50 generations (p. 37). He estimates that there are 5 times as many detrimental mutations as there are lethals (pp. 35-6). Thus, about a sixth might be expected to persist for 22 generations, the rest in excess of 50 generations.

If similar considerations apply to man, then one sixth of population A's mutant genes will be lethal; i.e., about 364,000, while B will contain 17,300 lethal genes. These will express themselves and be eliminated over a period of 22 generations. The vast majority of these, let us say in excess of 95 per cent, would involve recessive autosomal lethals. That means for 22 generations, each generation of population A would eliminate on the average of 15,700 (95 per cent of 364,000 divided by 22) such genes; while population B would similarly eliminate 748 such genes. These would express themselves, and hence be eliminated, primarily in the homozygous state. In the homozygous state, such recessive, autosomal lethal genes would result in miscarriages, stillbirths, neonatal and early childhood deaths, and deaths of individuals who had not reproduced, or were incapable of reproduction. An average of 7,850 such events would occur in each generation of population A, 374 in population B.

It is not likely that a recessive lethal has absolutely no effect at all in the heterozygous state. Thus, it is not proper to assume, as was done in the above calculation, that elimination occurs only if the lethal gene appears in the homozygous state. For this reason, the above figures may be increased by 10 per cent to account for the elimination of genes by the genetic deaths of partially handicapped, heterozygous individuals (Muller, 1957, pp. 36-7).

The effect of heterozygous elimination causes the rate of elimination to be much higher during the first few generations and much lower toward the 22nd generation. The rate of elimination is a function of the number of mutant genes present in any given generation.

The remaining 5 per cent lethal mutations would be recessive lethals on the sex chromosomes, or dominant lethals. These are likely to show up in the first generation. Therefore, one would expect 18,200 additional lethal genetic events of the sort described above in the first generation of population A, 865 in population B. Thus as a result of radiation-induced, lethal mutations, one may expect about 20,000 to 30,000 lethal genetic events in the first generation of population A, 1,000-1,500 of population B, and an average of 8,000-10,000 per generation for 22 generations in population A, 400-500 in population B. Both populations involve 1,000,000 individuals.

The theoretical considerations are in accord with the findings of Neel and Schull (1958), who studied the exposed Japanese populations (in Holifield, pp. 614-24). A reanalysis of their data reveals significant changes in the sex ratio of the children, which are caused by the production of recessive lethals on the X-chromosomes of irradiated mothers, and dominant lethals on the X-chromosomes of irradiated fathers. The former leads to the death of male progeny, the latter to the death of female progeny. The Japanese data support the estimate that the probability of inducing a sex-linked lethal mutation is of the order of 2.4×10^{-7} per rep (in Holifield, p. 623).* There was no evidence to demonstrate an effect of radiation exposure on the perinatal deaths or malformation frequency. Neel considers that such congenital malformations may be the segregants from complex homeostatic genetic systems. Mutations induced at loci involved in these homeostatic systems, while ultimately resulting in an increase in malformation frequency, would not be expected to bear the same simple and immediate relationship to malformation frequency as sex-linked mutations do to the sex ratio. Therefore, such an increase in congenital malformations would essentially be masked in the first post-bomb generation (ibid).

* That is, if 100,000,000 susceptible X-chromosome genes were to be irradiated so as to absorb a dose of 1 roentgen (or its physical equivalent, 1 rep), lethal mutations would be induced in about 24 such genes. If the dose were increased to 100 roentgens, then 2,400 such genes would undergo mutation. It is thought that the human X-chromosome has of the order of 250 genetic loci in which lethal mutations may occur. Therefore, 100,000,000 such susceptible X-chromosome genes involve 400,000 individuals. 2,400 lethal genetic events per 400,000 people exposed to 100 roentgens indicates a rate of 6 per thousand per 100 roentgens, a figure consistent with the Hiroshima data.

BIBLIOGRAPHY

Agricultural Research Service. *Radioactive Fallout in Time of Emergency: Effects upon Agriculture* (Special Report, A.R.S. 22-55). Washington, D.C.: U.S. Department of Agriculture, 1960.

Allison, A. C. "Aspects of Polymorphism in Man," *Cold Spring Harbor Symposium,* Vol. 20, 1955.

American Association for the Advancement of Science, Committee on Science in the Promotion of Human Welfare. "Science and Human Survival," *Science,* Vol. 134 (1961), pp. 2080-3.

Anderson, E. C., Ward, G. M., Holland, J. Z., and Langham, W. H. "Cesium-137 Levels in United States Powdered Milk and in the Population," in A. W. Klement, Jr. (ed.), *Radioactive Fallout from Nuclear Weapons Tests* (U.S. A.E.C. TID-7632). Washington, D.C.: U.S. Atomic Energy Commission, 1962.

Anderson, G. W., and Arnstein, M. G. *Communicable Disease Control,* 3rd ed. New York: The Macmillan Co., 1953.

Andrews, G. A. "Radiation Accidents," in John M. Fowler (ed.), *Fallout.* New York: Basic Books, 1960.

Auerbach, S. I. "Effect of Radiation on Ecological System of the Biosphere Due to Atomic Industry Operation" (Introductory Statement to a Report of the Study Group on the Co-ordination of Research Contracts on Selected Topics in Radiobiology). Vienna: International Atomic Energy Agency, 1961.

———. "Summary of Session, First National Symposium on Radioecology, 1961: Cycling in the Terrestrial Environment," in A. W. Klement, Jr. (ed.), *Radioactive Fallout from Nuclear Weapons Tests* (U.S. A.E.C. TID-7632). Washington, D.C.: U.S. Atomic Energy Commission, 1962.

———. "The Soil System and Radioactive Waste Disposal to the Ground," *Ecology*, Vol. 39 (1958), pp. 522-9.

Ayres, Robert U. "Effects of a Thermonuclear War on the Weather and Climate," in Tom Stonier (ed.), *Thermonuclear War: Some Effects on People and Nature*. New York: Blaisdell Publishing Co., in preparation.

Banfield, Edward C. *The Moral Basis of a Backward Society*. Glencoe, Illinois: The Free Press, 1958.

Barton, Allen H. *Social Organization Under Stress: A Sociological Review of Disaster Studies* (National Research Council Publication 1032). Washington, D.C.: National Academy of Sciences, 1963.

Beardsley, R. E. "Radiation Control," in *The Natural Philosopher*, Vol. 1. New York: Blaisdell Publishing Co., 1963.

Benton, A. H., and Werner, W. E., Jr. *Principles of Field Biology and Ecology*. New York: McGraw-Hill, 1958.

Benzaquin, Paul. *Holocaust*. New York: Henry Holt and Co., 1959.

Bergey's Manual of Determinative Bacteriology, 7th ed. Edited by R. S. Breed, E. G. D. Murray, and N. R. Smith. Baltimore, Maryland: Williams and Wilkins Co., 1957.

Biel, Erwin R. "Microclimate, Bioclimatology, and Notes on Comparative Dynamic Climatology," *American Scientist*, Vol. 49 (1961), pp. 326-57.

Bishopp, F. C., and Philip, C. B. "Carriers of Human Diseases," *Insects*, Yearbook of Agriculture, pp. 724-31. Washington, D.C.: U.S. Department of Agriculture, 1952.

Black, L. M. "How Insects Transmit Viruses," *Insects*, Yearbook of Agriculture, pp. 22-6. Ibid., 1953.

Blair, G. H., Vanden Brenk, H. A. S., Walter, J. B., and Slome, D. "Experimental Study of Effects of Radiation on Wound Healing," in D. Slome (ed.), *Wound Healing*. New York: Pergamon Press, 1961.

Bletchly, J. D., and Fisher, R. C. "Use of Gamma Radiation for the Destruction of Wood-Boring Insects," *Nature*, Vol. 179 (1957), p. 670.

Blum, H. F. "Environmental Radiation and Cancer," *Science*, Vol. 130 (1959), pp. 1545-7.

Bouillene, Raymond. "Man, the Destroying Biotype," *Science*, Vol. 135 (1962), pp. 706-12.

Bowen, G. D., and Rovira, A. D. "Plant Growth in Irradiated Soil," *Nature*, Vol. 191, No. 4791 (1961), pp. 936-7.

Braun, A. C. "A Demonstration of the Recovery of the Crown-Gall Tumor Cell with the Use of Complex Tumors of Single-Cell

Origin," *Proceedings of the National Academy of Sciences,* Vol. 45 (1959), pp. 932-8.

Bretz, T. W. "Oak Wilt, a New Threat," *Plant Diseases,* Yearbook of Agriculture, pp. 851-5. Washington, D.C.: U.S. Department of Agriculture, 1953.

Brewen, J. G. "X-Ray Induced Chromosome Aberrations in the Corneal Epithelium of the Chinese Hamster," *Science,* Vol. 138 (1962), pp. 820-2.

Broido, A. "Mass Fires Following Nuclear Attack," *Bulletin of the Atomic Scientists,* Vol. 16 (1960), pp. 409-13.

———, and McMasters, A. W. *The Influence of a Fire-Induced Convection Column on Radiological Fallout Patterns* (California Forest and Range Experimental Station Technical Paper 32). Berkeley, California: U.S. Department of Agriculture, Forest Service, 1959.

———. *Effects of Mass Fires on Personnel in Shelters* (Pacific Southwest Forest and Range Experimental Station Technical Paper 50). Ibid., 1960.

Brues, A. M. "Critique of the Linear Theory of Carcinogenesis," *Science,* Vol. 128 (1958), pp. 693-9.

Bucks, J. W., Evans, E. I., Ham, W. T., and Reid, J. D. "The Influence of External Body Radiation on Mortality from Thermal Burns," *Annals of Surgery,* Vol. 136 (1952), pp. 533-45.

Bulletin of the Atomic Scientists. "The First Pile," *Bulletin of the Atomic Scientists,* Vol. 18 (1962), pp. 19-24.

Burks, B. D. "Insects, Enemies of Insects," *Insects,* Yearbook of Agriculture, pp. 373-80. Washington, D.C.: U.S. Department of Agriculture, 1952.

Busch, Noel F. *Two Minutes to Noon.* New York: Simon and Schuster, 1962.

Business Fact Book, New York City. Albany, N. Y.: N. Y. Department of Commerce, 1957.

Business Fact Book, New York State. Ibid.

Caidin, M. *The Night Hamburg Died.* New York: Ballantine Books, 1960.

Callahan, E. D., Rosenblum, L., Kaplan, J. D., and Batten, D. R. *The Probable Fallout Threat Over the Continental United States* (Report TO-B, 60-13 prepared for the Office of Civil and Defense Mobilization). Burlington, Massachusetts: Technical Operations, Inc., 1960.

Christen, Robert J. "The Mongols in Mesopotamia: A Case History of the Destruction of a Technologically Advanced Society," in Tom Stonier (ed.), *Thermonuclear War: Some Effects on People and Nature.* New York: Blaisdell Publishing Co., in preparation.

Clark, P. G. *Vulnerability and Recuperation of a Regional Economy: A Study of the Impact of a Hypothetical Atomic Attack on New England* (Report RM-1809). Santa Monica, California: RAND Corporation, 1956.

Clebsch, A., Jr., and Lieberman, J. A. "The Possibility of Ground Water Contamination by Fallout," in A. W. Klement, Jr. (ed.), *Radioactive Fallout from Nuclear Weapons Tests* (U.S. A.E.C. TID-7632). Washington, D.C.: U.S. Atomic Energy Commission, 1962.

Coke, Richard. *Baghdad, the City of Peace.* London: Thornton Butterworth, Ltd., 1927.

Collins, Henry Hill, Jr. *America's Own Refugees.* Princeton, New Jersey: Princeton University Press, 1941.

Comar, C. L. "Biological Aspects of Nuclear War," *American Scientist*, Vol. 50, No. 2 (June 1962), pp. 339-53.

Conard, R. A., Huggins, C. E., Cannon, B., et al. "Medical Survey of Marshallese Two Years After Exposure to Fall-Out Radiation," *Journal of the American Medical Association*, Vol. 164 (1957), pp. 1192-7.

Conard, R. A., et al. *Medical Survey of Rongelap People Four Years After Exposure to Fallout* (Brookhaven National Laboratory Report BNL 534). Washington, D.C.: U.S. Department of Commerce, Office of Technical Services, 1959.

————. *Medical Survey of Rongelap People Five and Six Years After Exposure to Fallout* (Brookhaven Report BNL 609). Ibid., 1961.

————. *Medical Survey of Rongelap People Seven Years After Exposure to Fallout* (Brookhaven Report BNL 727). Ibid., 1962.

Corliss, J. M. "The Gypsy Moth," Yearbook of Agriculture, pp. 694-8. Washington, D.C.: U.S. Department of Agriculture, 1952.

Cornwell, P. B., Crook, L. J., and Bull, J. O. "Lethal and Sterilizing Effects of Gamma Radiation on Insects Infesting Cereal Commodities," *Nature*, Vol. 179 (1957), pp. 670-2.

Crick, F. H. C. "The Genetic Code," *Scientific American*, Vol. 207, No. 4 (1962), pp. 66-74.

Cronkite, E. P., Bond, V. P., and Dunham, C. L. (eds.). *The Effects of Ionizing Radiation on Human Beings: A Report of the Marshallese and Americans Accidentally Exposed to Radiation from Fallout and a Discussion of Radiation Injury in the Human Being.* Washington, D.C.: U.S. Government Printing Office, 1956.

Daubenmire, R. F. *Plants and Environment*, 2nd ed. New York: John Wiley and Sons, 1959.

Davis, R. J., Sheldon, V. L., and Auerbach, S. I. "Lethal Effects of Gamma Radiation upon Segments of a Natural Microbial Population," *Journal of Bacteriology*, Vol. 72 (1956), pp. 505-10.

Dobzhansky, Theodosius. "Man and Natural Selection," *American Scientist*, Vol. 49 (1961), pp. 285-99.

————. "Genetics, Society, and Evolution," *Bulletin of the New York Academy of Medicine*, Vol. 38 (1962), pp. 452-9.

Dubinin, N. P. *Problemy Radiacionnoi Genetiki*. Moscow: Gosatomizdat, 1961.

Dunaway, P. B., and Kay, S. V. "Effects of Ionizing Radiation on Mammal Populations on the White Oak Lake Bed," in V. Schultz and A. W. Klement, Jr. (eds.), *Proceedings of the First National Symposium on Radioecology*. New York: Reinhold Publishing Corp., 1963.

Dunn, F. L. "Pandemic Influenza in 1957: A Review of International Spread of New Asian Strain," *Journal of the American Medical Association*, Vol. 166 (1958), pp. 1140-8.

Edwards, R. D., and Williams, T. D. (eds.). *The Great Famine*. New York: New York University Press, 1957.

The Effects of Nuclear Weapons. Edited by S. Glasstone. Washington, D.C.: U.S. Department of Defense and U.S. Atomic Energy Commission, 1957.

————. Revised Edition, 1962.

Eisenbud, M., and Harley, J. H. "Long-Term Fallout," *Science*, Vol. 128, No. 3321 (August 22, 1958), pp. 399-402.

Elton, Charles S. *The Ecology of Invasions by Animals and Plants*. New York: John Wiley and Sons, 1958.

Enloe, Cortez F., Jr. "Nature of Air Raid Casualties," *Journal of the American Medical Association*, Vol. 147 (1951), pp. 858-62.

Eskey, C. R., and Haas, V. H. *Plague in the Western Part of the United States* (Public Health Bulletin 254). Washington, D.C.: U.S. Public Health Service, 1940.

Finnell, H. H. "The Dust Storms of 1954," *Scientific American*, Vol. 191, No. 1 (1954), pp. 25-9.

Fisher, Sydney N. *The Middle East: A History*. New York: Alfred A. Knopf, 1959.

Fletcher, N. H. *The Physics of Rainclouds*. Cambridge: Cambridge University Press, 1962.

Fosberg, F. R. "Plants and Fallout," *Nature*, Vol. 183 (1959), p. 1448.

Fowler, John M. (ed.). *Fallout*. New York: Basic Books, 1960.

Fritz, C. E., and Marks, E. S. "The NORC [National Opinion Research Center] Studies of Human Behavior in Disaster," *Journal of Social Issues*, Vol. 10, No. 3 (1954), pp. 26-41.

Fromm, Erich, and Maccoby, Michael. "A Debate on the Question of Civil Defense," *Commentary,* Vol. 33, No. 1 (January 1962), pp. 11-23; reprinted in *Breakthrough to Peace,* New York: New Directions, 1962.

Geiger, Rudolph. *The Climate Near the Ground.* Cambridge, Mass.: Harvard University Press, 1957.

Gell, P. G. H. Discussion on Nutrition and Resistance to Infection, *Proceedings of the Royal Society of Medicine,* Vol. 41 (1948), pp. 323-4.

Gelman, A. C. "The Ecology of Tularemia," in J. M. May (ed.), *Studies in Disease Ecology.* New York: Hafner Publishing Co., 1961.

Gentry, J. T., Parkhurst, E., and Bulin, G. V., Jr. "An Epidemiological Study of Congenital Malformation in New York State," *American Journal of Public Health,* Vol. 49, No. 4 (1959).

Glasstone, S. *Sourcebook on Atomic Energy,* 2nd ed. New York: D. Van Nostrand Co., 1958.

Grahn, O. "Genetic Alterations in Animals and Man," in B. B. Watson (ed.), *The Delayed Effects of Whole-Body Radiation.* Baltimore, Maryland: Johns Hopkins University Press, 1960.

Gravatt, G. F., and Parker, D. E. "Introduced Tree Diseases and Insects," *Trees,* Yearbook of Agriculture, pp. 446-51. Washington, D.C.: U.S. Department of Agriculture, 1949.

Green, E. R. R. "Agriculture," in R. D. Edwards and T. D. Williams (eds.), *The Great Famine.* New York: New York University Press, 1957.

Groves, Lieutenant-General Leslie R. *Now It Can Be Told.* New York: Harper & Brothers, 1962.

Grummitt, William E. "Strontium and Barium in Bone and Diet," in A. W. Klement, Jr. (ed.), *Radioactive Fallout from Nuclear Weapons Tests* (U.S. A.E.C. TID-7632). Washington, D.C.: U.S. Atomic Energy Commission, 1962.

Gunckel, J. E., and Sparrow, A. H. "Ionizing Radiations: Biochemical, Physiological and Morphological Aspects of Their Effects on Plants," in W. Ruhland (ed.), *Encyclopedia of Plant Physiology.* Berlin: Springer-Verlag, 1961.

Gustafsson, A. "The X-Ray Resistance of Dormant Seeds in Some Agricultural Plants," *Hereditas,* Vol. 30 (1944), pp. 165-78.

Hachiya, Michihiko. *Hiroshima Diary.* Translated and edited by W. Wells, M.D., Chapel Hill, North Carolina: University of North Carolina Press, 1955.

Harada, T., and Ishida, M. "Neoplasms Among A-Bomb Survivors in Hiroshima: First Report of the Research Committee on

Tumor Statistics, Hiroshima City Medical Association, Japan," *Journal of the National Cancer Institute,* Vol. 25 (1960), pp. 1253-64.

Hardy, A. V., and Watt, J. "Studies of the Acute Diarrheal Diseases: XVIII, Epidemiology," *Public Health Reports,* Vol. 63 (1948), pp. 363-78.

Harrington, D., and Fene, W. J. *Barricading as a Life-Saving Measure in Connection with Mine Fires and Explosions* (Miners' Circular 42). Washington, D.C.: U.S. Department of the Interior, Bureau of Mines, 1941.

Hawkins, M. B. *Procedures for the Assessment and Control of the Shorter-Term Hazards of Nuclear Warfare Fallout in Water Supply Systems* (Civil Defense Research Project 2 [34]). Berkeley, California: University of California, Institute of Engineering Research, 1960.

Henderson, Brigadier General F. P. "Quest for Survival," *Ordnance,* Vol. 47 (Sept.-Oct. 1962), pp. 159-61.

Hersey, John. *Hiroshima.* New York: Alfred A. Knopf, 1946.

Hewlett, R. G., and Anderson, O. E., Jr. *The New World, 1939-1946,* Vol. 1, *A History of the United States Atomic Energy Commission.* University Park, Pennsylvania: Pennsylvania State University Press, 1962.

Hirst, L. F. *The Conquest of Plague.* New York: Oxford University Press, 1953.

Holifield, Congressman Chet. Hearings Before the Special Subcommittee on Radiation, Joint Committee on Atomic Energy, Congress of the United States.

　　Fallout from Nuclear Weapons Tests. May 1959.

　　Biological and Environmental Effects of Nuclear War. June 1959.

———. Hearings Before the Subcommittee on Military Operations, Committee on Government Operations, House of Representatives of the United States.

　　Civil Defense. March 1960.

　　Civil Defense—1961. August 1961.

Hollis, M. D., and Fellton, H. L. "Post-War Control of Flies and Mosquitoes on Public Health Programs," *American Journal of Public Health,* Vol. 36 (1946), pp. 1432-6.

Hollingsworth, J. W. "Delayed Radiation Effects in Survivors of the Atomic Bombings," *New England Journal of Medicine,* Vol. 263 (1960), pp. 481-7.

Humphreys, W. J. *Physics of the Air,* 2nd ed. New York: McGraw-Hill, 1929.

———. 3rd ed., 1940.

Huxley, Aldous. *Ape and Essence.* New York: Harper, 1948.

Iklé, F. C. *The Social Impact of Bomb Destruction.* Norman, Oklahoma: University of Oklahoma Press, 1958.

———. "Nth Countries and Disarmament," *Bulletin of the Atomic Scientists,* Vol. 16 (1960), pp. 391-4.

Ingersoll, J. M. "An Example of Ecological Devastation and Recovery: Krakatau," in Tom Stonier (ed.), *Thermonuclear War: Some Effects on People and Nature.* New York: Blaisdell Publishing Co., in preparation.

Jamaica Water Supply Company. *A Picture of Your Water Company* (Annual Report and Brochure). Jamaica, New York, 1959.

Janis, Irving L. "Problems of Theory in the Analysis of Stress Behavior," *Journal of Social Issues,* Vol. 10, No. 3 (1954), pp. 12-25.

Kalmbach, E. R. "Birds, Beasts, and Bugs," Yearbook of Agriculture, pp. 724-31. Washington, D.C.: U.S. Department of Agriculture, 1952.

Keen, F. P. "Bark Beetles in Forests," *Insects,* Yearbook of Agriculture, pp. 688-94. Ibid.

———. "Pine Bark Beetles," *Trees,* Yearbook of Agriculture, pp. 427-32. Ibid., 1949.

King, R. C. *Genetics.* New York: Oxford University Press, 1962.

King, R. C., Darrow, J. B., and Kaye, N. W. "Studies on Different Classes of Mutations Induced by Radiation on *Drosophila melanogaster* Females," *Genetics,* Vol. 41 (1956), pp. 890-900.

Kulp, J. L., and Schulert, A. R. "Strontium-90 in Man, V," *Science,* Vol. 136 (1962), pp. 619-32.

Langer, William L. "The Next Assignment," *The American Historical Review,* Vol. 63 (January 1958), pp. 283-304.

Langham, W. H. Comments in A. W. Klement, Jr. (ed.), *Radioactive Fallout from Nuclear Weapons Tests* (U.S. A.E.C. TID-7632). Washington, D.C.: U.S. Atomic Energy Commission, 1962.

Lapp, Ralph E. "Nuclear Weapons and Civil Defense," Speech Before Ford Hall Forum, Boston, Massachusetts, October 8, 1961.

Laverty, Maura. "Women-Shy Irishmen," in John A. O'Brien (ed.), *The Vanishing Irish.* New York: McGraw-Hill, 1953.

Lawson, F. R. "Some Features of the Relation of Insects to Their Ecosystem," *Ecology,* Vol. 39 (1958), pp. 515-21.

Leach, J. G. "Bacteria, Fungi, and Insects," Yearbook of Agriculture, pp. 63-7. Washington, D.C.: U.S. Department of Agriculture, 1953.

Leasor, James. *The Plague and the Fire.* New York: McGraw-Hill, 1961.

Leiderman, P. H., and Mendelson, J. H. "Some Psychiatric and Social Aspects of the Defense-Shelter Program," Part IV of series "The Medical Consequences of Nuclear War," *New England Journal of Medicine*, Vol. 266 (1962), pp. 1126-55, 1174.

Leontief, W. W., and Hoffenberg, M. "The Economic Effects of Disarmament," *Scientific American*, Vol. 214 (1961), pp. 47-55.

Libby, W. F. "Radioactive Fallout," *Proceedings of the National Academy of Sciences*, Vol. 44 (1958), pp. 800-20.

Link, V. B. *A History of Plague in the United States* (Public Health Bulletin 392). Washington, D.C.: U.S. Public Health Service, 1955.

Lord, Walter. *A Night to Remember*. New York: Henry Holt and Co., 1955.

Lowdermilk, W. C. *Conquest of the Land Through 7,000 Years* (Agricultural Information Bulletin 99). Washington, D.C.: U.S. Department of Agriculture, 1953.

———. "The Reclamation of Man-Made Desert," *Scientific American*, Vol. 202 (1960), pp. 55-63.

Lüning, K. G., Frölén, H., Nelson, A., and Rönnbäck, C. "Genetic Effects of Strontium-90 Injected into Male Mice," *Nature*, Vol. 197 (1963), pp. 304-5.

MacArthur, Sir William P. "Medical History of the Famine," in R. D. Edwards and T. D. Williams (eds.), *The Great Famine*. New York: New York University Press, 1957.

McCormick, J. F., and Platt, R. B. "Effects of Ionizing Radiation on a Natural Plant Community," in V. Schultz and A. W. Klement, Jr. (eds.), *Proceedings of the First National Symposium on Radioecology*. New York: Reinhold Publishing Corp., 1963.

MacDonagh, O. "Irish Emigration to the United States of America and the British Colonies During the Famine," in R. D. Edwards and T. D. Williams (eds.), *The Great Famine*. New York: New York University Press, 1957.

McDowell, R. B. "Ireland on the Eve of the Famine," in Ibid.

McHugh, Robert J. "The Famine in Irish Oral Tradition," in Ibid.

MacMahon, B. "Prenatal X-Ray Exposure and Childhood Cancer," *Journal of the National Cancer Institute*, Vol. 28 (1962), pp. 1173-91.

Marcovich, H. "Etude Radiobiologique du Système Lysogène d'*Escherichia coli* K12" (Thèse des Sciences, No. 3846, 1957) in *Report of the United Nations Scientific Committee on the Effects of Atomic Radiation*, 1962.

Martell, E. A. "Atmospheric Aspects of Strontium-90 Fallout," *Science*, Vol. 129 (1959), pp. 1197-1206.

Medical Effects of the Atomic Bomb in Japan. A. W. Oughterson and S. Warren. New York: McGraw-Hill, 1956.

Meerloo, Joost A. M. "People's Reaction to Danger," in Iago Galdston and Hans Zetterberg (eds.), *Panic and Morale.* New York: International Universities Press, 1958.

Melman, Seymour (ed.). *Inspection for Disarmament.* New York: Columbia University Press, 1958.

――――. Speech presented to the American Association for the Advancement of Science, Denver, Colorado, December 26, 1961.

Miller, Walter M., Jr. *A Canticle for Leibowitz.* Philadelphia: J. B. Lippincott Co., 1959.

Milne, Loros J., and Milne, Margery. *The Balance of Nature.* New York: Alfred A. Knopf, 1960.

Mitchell, H. H. "Ecological Problems and Postwar Recuperation: A Preliminary Survey from the Civil Defense Viewpoint" (RAND Research Memorandum, RM-2801-PR). Santa Monica, Calif.: The RAND Corporation, 1961.

Morris, R. F., Cheshire, W. F., Miller, C. A., and Mott, D. G. "The Numerical Response of Avian and Mammalian Predators During a Gradation of the Spruce Budworm," *Ecology,* Vol. 39 (1958), pp. 487-94.

Muller, H. J. "Damage from Point Mutations in Relation to Radiation Dose and Biological Conditions," in *Effect of Radiation on Human Heredity.* Geneva: World Health Organization, 1957.

Murray, Edmund J. "The Key to the Problem," in John A. O'Brien (ed.), *The Vanishing Irish.* New York: McGraw-Hill, 1953.

Myers, R. F., and Dropkin, V. H. "Impracticability of Control of Plant Parasitic Nematodes with Ionizing Radiations," *Plant Disease Reporter,* Vol. 43 (1959), pp. 311-13.

Nagai, Takashi. *We of Nagasaki.* Translated by I. Shirato and H. B. L. Silverman. New York: Duell, Sloan and Pearce, 1951.

Nagan, P. S. (ed.). *Medical Almanac, 1961-2.* Philadelphia: W. B. Saunders Co., 1962.

National Academy of Sciences, National Research Council. *The Biological Effects of Atomic Radiation: A Report to the Public.* Washington, D.C.: National Academy of Sciences, 1956.

――――. *The Biological Effects of Atomic Radiation: Summary Reports.* Ibid., 1960.

National Academy of Sciences, Committee on Pathologic Effects of Atomic Radiation. *Effects of Inhaled Radioactive Particles* (National Research Council Publication 848). Ibid., 1961.

――――. *Long-Term Effects of Ionizing Radiations from External Sources* (National Research Council Publication 849). Ibid.

National Bureau of Standards. *Maximum Permissible Amounts*

of Radioisotopes in the Human Body and Maximum Permissible Concentrations in Air and Water (National Committee on Radiation Protection Handbook 52), 1953.

———. *Radioactive-Waste Disposal in the Ocean* (Handbook 58), 1954.

Neel, J. V., and Schull, W. J. *The Effect of Exposure to the Atomic Bombs on Pregnancy Termination in Hiroshima and Nagasaki* (National Research Council Publication 461). Washington, D.C.: National Academy of Sciences, 1956.

Neiland, B. J. "Forest and Adjacent Burn in the Tillamook Burn Area of Northwestern Oregon," *Ecology*, Vol. 39 (1958), pp. 660-71.

New York Weather Almanac. New York: Consolidated Edison, 1963.

Nirenberg, M. W. "The Genetic Code: II," *Scientific American*, Vol. 208, No. 3 (1963), pp. 80-94.

Nordlie, Peter G., and Popper, Robert D. *Social Phenomena in a Post-Nuclear-Attack Situation*. Arlington, Virginia: Champion Press, 1961.

Nowlan, Kevin B. "The Political Background," in R. D. Edwards and T. D. Williams (eds.), *The Great Famine*. New York: New York University Press, 1957.

O'Brien, John A. (ed.). *The Vanishing Irish*. New York: McGraw-Hill, 1953.

Odum, E. P., in collaboration with H. T. Odum. *Fundamentals of Ecology*. Philadelphia: W. B. Saunders Co., 1959.

Office of Civil and Defense Mobilization. *Fire Effects of Bombing Attacks* (Technical Manual 9-2), 1955.

O'Neill, T. P. "The Organization and Administration of Relief, 1845-52," in R. D. Edwards and T. D. Williams (eds.), *The Great Famine*. New York: New York University Press, 1957.

Oosting, H. J. *The Study of Plant Communities*, 2nd ed. San Francisco: W. H. Freeman, 1956.

Orear, J. "The Detection of Nuclear Weapons Testing," in Seymour Melman (ed.), *Inspection for Disarmament*. New York: Columbia University Press, 1958.

Palumbo, R. F. "Recovery of the Land Plants at Eniwetok Atoll Following a Nuclear Detonation," *Radiation Botany*, Vol. 1 (1962), pp. 182-9.

Parker, R. R., Steinhaus, E. A., Kohls, G. M., and Jellison, W. L. *Contamination of Natural Waters and Mud with Pasteurella Tularensis and Tularemia in Beaver and Muskrats in Northwestern United States* (National Institute of Health Bulletin 193). Washington, D.C.: U.S. Government Printing Office, 1951.

Pedigo, R. A. "Effects of Ionizing Radiation on *Pinus Taeda* (L)," in V. Schultz and A. W. Klement, Jr. (eds.), *Proceedings of the First National Symposium on Radioecology.* New York: Reinhold Publishing Corp., 1963.

Platt, R. B. "Ecological Effects of Ionizing Radiation on Organisms, Communities, and Ecosystems," in Ibid.

Pollitzer, R., and Meyer, K. F. "The Ecology of Plague," in J. M. May (ed.), *Studies in Disease Ecology.* New York: Hafner Publishing Co., 1961.

"Positive Plague and Tularemia Specimens Reported in Canada During 1942," *Public Health Reports,* Vol. 58 (1943), p. 646.

Puck, T. T. "Action of Radiation on Mammalian Cells: III, Relationship Between Reproductive Death and Induction of Chromosome Anomalies by X-Irradiation of Euploid Human Cells *in Vitro*," *Proceedings of the National Academy of Sciences,* Vol. 44 (1958), pp. 772-80.

Puck, T. T., Morkovin, D., Marcus, P. I., and Cieciura, S. J. "Action of X-rays on Mammalian Cells: II, Survival Curves of Cells from Normal Human Tissues," *Journal of Experimental Medicine,* Vol. 106 (1957), pp. 485-500.

Rhode, C. J. "Studies on the Biologies of Two Mite Species, Predator and Prey, Including Some Effects of Gamma Radiation on Selected Developmental Stages," *Ecology,* Vol. 40 (1959), pp. 572-9.

Rugh, R. "Vertebrate Radiobiology (Embryology)," *Annual Review of Nuclear Science,* Vol. 9 (1959), pp. 493-522.

Russell, W. L., and Kelly, E. M. "Comparison Between Mutation Rates Induced by Chronic Gamma and Acute X-Irradiation in Mice," *Science,* Vol. 127 (1958), p. 1062.

Sacher, G. *Proceedings of the Gatlinburg Conference on the Biological Aspects of Aging, 1957.* Washington, D.C.: American Institute of Biological Science, 1959.

Schaefer, M. B., et al. "Oceanographic Studies During Operation 'Wigwam,'" Supplement to Volume VII, 1962, of *Limnology and Oceanography.*

Schmidt, B. "Der Einbruch der Tularämie in Europa," *Zeitschrift für Hygiene und Infektionskrankheiten,* Vol. 127 (1947), pp. 139-50.

Schull, W. J., and Neel, J. V. "Radiation and the Sex Ratio in Man," *Science,* Vol. 128 (1958), pp. 343-8.

Sears, Paul B. *Deserts on the March,* 3rd ed. Norman, Oklahoma: University of Oklahoma Press, 1959.

Selleck, G. W., and Schuppert, K. "Some Aspects of Microclimate in a Pine Forest and in an Adjacent Prairie," *Ecology*, Vol. 38 (1957), pp. 650-3.

Seymour, A. "Summary of Reports on Fallout Nuclides in the Marine Environment Presented at the 1961 Radioecology Symposium," in A. W. Klement, Jr. (ed.), *Radioactive Fallout from Nuclear Weapons Tests* (U.S. A.E.C. TID-7632). Washington, D.C.: U.S. Atomic Energy Commission, 1962.

Sheridan, John D. "We're Not Dead Yet," in John A. O'Brien (ed.), *The Vanishing Irish*. New York: McGraw-Hill, 1953.

Shope, R. E. "Influenza: History, Epidemiology, and Speculation," *Public Health Reports*, Vol. 73 (1958), pp. 165-78.

———. "Old, Intermediate, and Contemporary Contribution to Our Knowledge of Pandemic Influenza," *Medicine*, Vol. 23 (1944), pp. 415ff.

Sidel, V. W., Geiger, H. J., and Lown, B. "The Medical Consequences of Thermonuclear War: II, The Physician's Role in the Postattack Period," *New England Journal of Medicine*, Vol. 266 (1962), pp. 1137-45.

Simak, R., and Gustafsson, A. "X-Ray Photography and Sensitivity in Forest Tree Species," *Hereditas*, Vol. 39 (1953), pp. 458-68.

Smillie, W. G. *Preventive Medicine and Public Health*, 2nd ed. New York: The Macmillan Co., 1952.

Sparrow, A. H., and Woodwell, G. M. "Prediction of the Sensitivity of Plants to Chronic Gamma Irradiation," *Radiation Botany*, Vol. 2 (1962), pp. 9-26.

Sparrow, A. H., Cuany, R. L., Miksche, J. P., and Schairer, L. A. "Some Factors Affecting the Response of Plants to Acute and Chronic Radiation Exposure," Ibid., Vol. 1 (1961), pp. 10-34.

Spector, William S. *Handbook of Biological Data*. Ohio: Wright-Patterson Air Force Base, 1956.

Statistical Abstract of the United States, 82nd annual ed. Washington, D.C.: Department of Commerce, Bureau of Census, 1961.

———. 83rd annual ed. Ibid., 1962.

Steinhaus, E. A. "Crowding as a Possible Stress Factor in Insect Diseases," *Ecology*, Vol. 39 (1958), pp. 503-14.

Stoeckeler, J. H. *Shelterbelt Influence on Great Plains Field Environment and Crops* (Production Research Report 62). Washington, D.C.: U.S. Department of Agriculture, Forest Service, 1962.

Stone, E. S., Wheeler, M. R., Spencer, W. P., et al. "Genetic Studies of Irradiated Natural Populations of *Drosophila*," *Studies in the Genetics of Drosophila*, University of Texas Publication 5721 (1957).

Stonier, T. *Anticipated Biological and Environmental Effects of*

Detonating a 20-Megaton Weapon on Columbus Circle, New York. Annals of the New York Academy of Sciences, Vol. 105, No. 5 (1963), pp. 287-382.

——. "Labeling Crown Gall Bacteria with P^{32} for Radioautography," *Journal of Bacteriology*, Vol. 72 (1956), pp. 259-68.

—— (ed.). *Thermonuclear War: Some Effects on People and Nature.* New York: Blaisdell Publishing Co., in preparation.

——, Beardsley, R. E., Lipetz, J., and Socolar, S. *Radiation, Its Biological Effects, and the Fallout Problem.* New York: Scientists' Committee for Radiation Information, 1960.

Stowman, Knud. "Synopsis of Epidemics in Europe," *Epidemic Information Bulletin*, Vol. 2 (1946), pp. 323-32, 413-22, 493-502.

——. "Typhus During the War," Ibid., Vol. 1 (1945), pp. 289-310.

Strategic Bombing Survey, Morale Division. *The Effect of Bombing on Health and Medical Care in Germany* (Medical Branch Report). Washington, D.C.: War Department, 1945.

——, Overall Economic Effects Division. *The Effects of Strategic Bombing on the German War Economy.* Ibid.

Strehler, Bernard L. "Origin and Comparison of the Effects of Time and High-Energy Radiations on Living Systems," *Quarterly Review of Biology*, Vol. 34 (1959), pp. 117-42.

Strom, P. L., Mackin, J. L., Macdonald, D., and Zigman, P. E. "Long-Lived Cobalt Isotopes Observed in Fallout," *Science*, Vol. 128 (1958), pp. 417-19.

Thale, T., and Opper, L. "Factors Affecting the Susceptibility to Bacillary Dysentery," *American Journal of Public Health*, Vol. 36 (1946), pp. 1150-5.

Titmuss, Richard M. *Problems of Social Policy.* London: His Majesty's Stationery Office, 1950.

Trevelyan, G. M. *English Social History*, 3rd ed. London: Longmans, Green and Co., 1946.

——. History of England, 2nd ed. Ibid., 1937.

United Nations Scientific Committee. *Report of the United Nations Scientific Committee on the Effects of Atomic Radiation.* New York: United Nations, 1958.

——. Ibid., 1962.

Vereinigung Deutscher Wissenschaftler. *Ziviler Bevolkerungsschutz Heute.* Hamburg-Blankenese: H. Afheldt, Strandweg 57, 1962.

Wallace, B., and Dobzhansky, Theodosius. *Radiation, Genes, and Man.* New York: Henry Holt and Co., 1959.

Weaver, J. E. "Summary and Interpretation of Underground Development in Natural Grassland Communities," *Ecological Monographs,* Vol. 28 (1958), pp. 55-78.

Weiss, P. "The Life History of the Neuron," *Journal of Chronic Diseases,* Vol. 3 (1956), pp. 340-8.

Wexler, H. "Radiation Balance of the Earth as a Factor in Climatic Change," in Harlow Shapley (ed.), *Climatic Change, Evidence, Causes and Effects.* Cambridge, Mass.: Harvard University Press, 1953.

Wheeler, C. M. "Control of Typhus in Italy, 1943-1944, by Use of DDT," *American Journal of Public Health,* Vol. 36 (1946), pp. 119-29.

Winkler, C. *Statistical Guide for New York City, 1959,* 3rd ed. New York: New York Department of Commerce and Public Events, 1959.

Woodwell, G. M. "Effects of Ionizing Radiation on Terrestrial Ecosystems," *Science,* Vol. 138 (1962), pp. 572-7.

———. "Effects of Ionizing Radiation on Natural Ecosystems," in Tom Stonier (ed.), *Thermonuclear War: Some Effects on People and Nature.* New York: Blaisdell Publishing Co., in preparation.

Works Progress Administration. *Depression Pioneers.* Washington, D.C.: Works Progress Administration, 1939.

World Health Organization. *Effects of Radiation on Human Heredity.* Geneva: World Health Organization, 1957.

Wright, S. "On the Appraisal of Genetic Effects of Radiation in Man," in *The Biological Effects of Atomic Radiation.* Washington, D.C.: National Academy of Science, National Research Council, 1960.

Wu, Lien-Teh. *Plague Fighter: The Autobiography of a Modern Chinese Physician.* Cambridge, England: W. Heffer & Sons, 1959.

Wygant, N. D., and Nelson, A. L. "Four Billion Feet of Beetle-Killed Spruce," *Trees,* Yearbook of Agriculture, pp. 417-22. Washington, D.C.: U.S. Department of Agriculture, 1949.

Yee, H. L. S. *Test Report: Shelter Life Support System.* Strykersville, N.Y.: A. J. Sawyer Co., 1961.

Zinsser, H. *Microbiology,* 12th ed. Edited by D. T. Smith, N. F. Conant, et al. New York: Appleton-Century-Crofts, 1960.

NOTES

Sources, which are given in full in the Bibliography, are cited here by the last name of the author. Dates are included only when it is necessary to distinguish between two works by the same author. When there is more than one work by the same author published in the same year, the letters "a" or "b" follow the date and correspond to the order in which the titles appear in the Bibliography. The May 1959 Holifield hearing is referred to as *Holifield Fallout;* the June 1959 hearing is referred to as *Holifield.* The following sources appear in abbreviated form:

ARS	Agricultural Research Service
BFB, NYC	Business Fact Book, New York City
BFB, NYS	Business Fact Book, New York State
ENW	Effects of Nuclear Weapons
MEJ	Medical Effects of the Atomic Bomb in Japan
NAS	National Academy of Sciences
OCDM	Office of Civil and Defense Mobilization
PHR	Public Health Reports
SBS	Strategic Bombing Survey
WHO	World Health Organization

CHAPTER 1

P. 17. Death statistics: *Stat. Abs. 1962,* table 343, p. 257.
P. 17. Fromm and Maccoby: *Fromm and Maccoby,* 19.
Pp. 17-18. "Retired Marine Brigadier . . . of the civilian population": *Henderson,* 160.

P. 18. Death statistics: *Vereinigung Deutscher Wissenschaftler*, 1.

P. 18. Account of "Operation Gomorrah": *OCDM*, 1–2; *Caidin*, 119.

Pp. 18–19. "The Hamburg attack . . . almost inevitable": *OCDM*, 1, 3, 20, 22.

P. 19. "Shortly before the outbreak . . . became involved": *Hewlett and Anderson*, 10, 12, 13, 22.

Pp. 19–20. "In the meantime . . . the research" and first footnote, p. 20: *Ibid.*, 20.

P. 20. "The pace . . . controlled it": *Bulletin of the Atomic Scientists.*

P. 20. Groves memorandum: *Groves*, 433.

P. 20. Hiroshima and Nagasaki bombings: *ENW 1962*, 672; *Hewlett and Anderson*, 401–4.

P. 20. Second footnote: *Groves*, 324.

Pp. 20–1. BRAVO shot: *ENW 1962*, 673; *Andrews*, 108.

P. 21. First footnote: *ENW 1962*, 673.

P. 21. Second footnote: *Fowler*, 15–17.

Pp. 21–2. "This large detonation . . . products (fallout)": *Holifield*, 17, 44; *ENW*, 6, 33.

P. 22. Twenty-megaton explosion: *ENW 1962*, 29, 44–45, 76, 316, 330, 333, 358–9, 363, 366, 557; *ENW*, 337; *MEJ*, 14.

P. 22. Second footnote: *ENW*, 391, 435; *Holifield Fallout*, 1971, 2427, calculations from data on 1978; *Libby*, 816; calculations based on formulae from *Glasstone*, 519, 521.

P. 22. Third footnote: *Holifield*, 846, map opposite p. 12.

Pp. 22–3. One-megaton fireball: *ENW 1962*, 30, 34, 35, 36, 76–7.

P. 23. "Meanwhile, a huge pressure . . . twenty miles across": *ENW 1962*, 42–3, 107, 363, 366.

P. 23. "In a contact . . . could be shattered": *ENW*, 87, 230, 248–9.

CHAPTER 2

P. 25. "On a very clear day . . . twenty miles away": *ENW*, 337, 339.

Pp. 25–6. "In both Hiroshima and Nagaski . . . be 70 per cent": *MEJ*, 94, 102, 103.

P. 26. Footnote: *ENW 1962*, 332.

Pp. 26–7. "Similarly, at Hiroshima's . . . 40 per cent": *MEJ*, 104; *ENW*, 337, 339; *Holifield*, 234–6.

P. 27. Ham and Pickering: *Holifield*, 250, 285, 298.

P. 27. 300 roentgens: *ENW*, 352.

P. 27. Communication Center: *MEJ*, 61–2.

P. 27. Footnote (450 roentgens): *Holifield*, 31; definition of roentgen: *ENW 1962*, 711–12.

Pp. 27–8. "In Hiroshima and Nagasaki . . . in the same way": *MEJ*, 99; *ENW*, Chapter 3.

P. 28. Earthquake shock: *Orear.*

P. 28. Dimensions of hole (in both text and footnote): *ENW 1962*, 289–93.

P. 29. "At the 7.5-mile . . . 60 mph": *ENW*, 101, 108–9; *Holifield*, 338.

P. 29. Nevada test site: *Lapp 1961.*

Pp. 29–32. Extent of damage in inner zone: *Holifield*, 25; *ENW*, 86, 111, 127, 133, 246–9, 508.

P. 32. Damage in outer zone (lines 4–9): *ENW*, 127–8.

P. 32. Window breakage 40 miles away: *ENW*, 73, 232.
P. 32. "For example, . . . 100 miles away": *ENW*, 87.
Pp. 33–4. White's testimony on blast effects: *Holifield*, 326, 327, 351–3.
P. 33. First footnote: *ENW*, 107.

CHAPTER 3

P. 35. Lines 1–10: *OCDM*, iii.
Pp. 35–6. "There are two . . . point of detonation": *ENW*, 295, 316–18.
P. 36. Definition of firestorm: *ENW*, 327.
P. 36. Definition of conflagration: *OCDM*, 7.
Pp. 36–7. Hiroshima firestorm: *Holifield*, 238–41; *ENW*, 326–7; *Broido*, 413 (citing Strategic Bombing Survey).
P. 37. Mr. Mizoguchi: *Hachiya*, 77–8.
Pp. 37–8. Dr. Hanaoka: *Ibid.*, 19–20.
P. 38. Nagasaki: *ENW*, 326–7.
P. 38. Few mechanical injuries: *MEJ*, 2.
P. 38. Hamburg firestorm: *OCDM*, 2.
Pp. 38–9. Consulting pathologist's report: *SBSa*, 20.
P. 39. "The Fire Effects of Bombing Attacks": *OCDM*, 2.
Pp. 39–40. Shelter deaths: *SBSa*, 21–3.
Pp. 40–1. Enloe report: *Enloe*.
Pp. 41–2. "In addition . . . carbon monoxide poisoning": *SBSa*, 25.
P. 42. Death from inhalation: *Broido and McMasters 1960*, 26.
P. 42. National Bureau of Standards tests (lines 11–25): *Ibid.*, 4, 21; *SBSa*, fig. 4, p. 15.
Pp. 42–3. Data from experimental fires: *Broido and McMasters 1960*, 9, 13–15, 21, 22, 78.
P. 43. German cities: *OCDM*, 2.
P. 43. Potassium superoxide: *Yee*.
P. 43. "In the absence . . . per hour": *Harrington and Fene*, 9.
P. 44. "At this point . . . spread of fires": *ENW*, 325; *MEJ*, fig. 3.42, p. 63.
Pp. 44–5. Building density and comparison of American, German, and Japanese cities: *OCDM*, 18–22.
P. 46. "Studies conducted . . . 100 square miles": *Broido*, 412; *OCDM*, 24–5.

CHAPTER 4

P. 47. "Overt actions . . . ordinarily disregarded": *Janis*, 18.
P. 47. Footnote: *Meerloo*, 175–6.
Pp. 47–8. Iklé: *Iklé 1958*, 101, 103.
P. 48. Definition of panic: cited in *Nordlie and Popper*, 16.
P. 48. "Panic usually . . . blocked" and footnote: *Iklé 1958*, 101, 103.
P. 48. Cocoanut Grove fire: *Benzaquin*, 47–8, 56–7, 60.
P. 48. Fall of France: *Meerloo*, 174–5.
P. 48. "After the atomic . . . stations": *MEJ*, 23.
Pp. 48–9. "The term . . . operation": *Nordlie and Popper*, 18 (citing Janis 1951).
P. 49. "If the behavior . . . trapped neighbors": *Hersey*, 38, 40.
P. 49. Dr. Nagai: *Nagai*, 4, 187.
P. 49. Behavior of disaster victims: *Janis*, 19.

Pp. 49–50. Dr. Hachiya: *Hachiya*, 54–5.

P. 50. *Titanic*: *Lord*, 120-2.

Pp. 50–1. "Fear for one's own . . . in these small groups": *Nordlie and Popper*, 32 (citing Logan et al. 1950).

P. 51. "The most . . . crisis situation": *Ibid.* (citing Fritz and Williams 1957).

P. 51. "During the actual . . . strangers": *Ibid.*, 31–2 (citing Thompson and Hawkes and University of Chicago National Opinion Research Center 1953).

P. 51. Next-to-last paragraph: *Ibid.* (citing Fritz and Mathewson 1957, Logan et al. 1950, Univ. of Chicago NORC 1953, and Fogleman and Parenton 1959); Professor Allen H. Barton, personal communication.

Pp. 51–2. Hiroshima: *Hachiya*, 22.

P. 52. Prolonged fear: *Nordlie and Popper*, 31 (citing Janis 1951).

P. 52. "The pattern of fear . . . relief activity": *Janis*, 20.

P. 52. Footnote: *Fritz and Marks*, 34.

CHAPTER 5

P. 53. Twenty-megaton explosion: based on extrapolations from Fig. 4.3, *Callahan et al.*, 106.

Pp. 53–5. "Fallout injuries can be . . . as 225 roentgens": *Cronkite et al.*, 100–3.

P. 55. LD_{50} = 450 roentgens: *Holifield*, 31.

Pp. 55–6. National Academy of Sciences: *NAS 1961b*, 7.

Pp. 56–7. "Individuals exposed to . . . the combined injury": *Cronkite et al.*, 101–3.

P. 57. Marshall Islanders' symptoms: *Ibid.*, 27–8, 31.

P. 57. "The deposition . . . much greater importance": *Ibid.*, 3.

P. 58. "In human beings . . . evidence at present": *NAS 1961a*, 76.

P. 58. Footnote: *Holifield*, 44; *ENW 1962*, 437.

P. 59. Lapp on weathering: *Holifield*, 211, 221-3.

P. 60. Table: *ENW*, 402.

Pp. 60–1. Shielding factors in various buildings: *Holifield*, 161.

P. 61. Foxhole: *ENW 1962*, 473.

CHAPTER 6

P. 66. Footnote ("The 1959 . . . without injury"): *Holifield*, 846, 853; *BFB, NYC*, 15; World War II: *Iklé 1958*, 24.

Pp. 67–9. *Medical Effects of the Atomic Bomb in Japan* report (to line 5, p. 69): *MEJ*, 71–2, 75.

P. 69. Location of Communications Hospital: *MEJ*, map inside front cover.

P. 69. "Although the second . . . more than that": *Hachiya*, 7, 9–12.

Pp. 69–70. *MEJ* quote: *MEJ*, 77.

P. 70. Hachiya: *Hachiya*, 11–12, 117–18.

Pp. 70–1. "Conditions were not . . . have been prevented": *MEJ*, 76, 78.

P. 71. Footnote: *Holifield*, 847, 853; *Stat. Abs. 1962*, 66.

P. 71. RAND Corporation: *P. G. Clark*, iii.

Pp. 71–2. Germany: *SBSa*, 338–9, 348.

P. 72. *New England Journal of Medicine*: *Sidel, Geiger, and Lown*.

P. 72. Untreated burn wounds: *Holifield*, 252.

P. 72. Tetanus: *SBSa*, 23.

Pp. 72–3. Infection in Japan: *MEJ*, 101.

P. 73. "Cells of . . . 100 roentgens": *Puck et al.*

P. 73. Tokyo and first footnote: *MEJ*, 101.

P. 73. National Damage Assessment Center: *Holifield*, 858.

P. 73. Second footnote (casualty figures): *Ibid.*, 847, 852; Hardin Jones: *Ibid.*, 592.

P. 73. Storing in target areas: *Ibid.*, 253.

P. 74. "Drs. Sidel . . . 40,000,000 injured": *Sidel, Geiger, and Lown.*

P. 74. Footnote: *Holifield*, 847, 853; *Holifield Civil Defense 1960*, 112.

CHAPTER 7

P. 75. Water-pipe breaks: *OCDM*, 15; *Broido*, 413.

P. 75. "Water supplies . . . contamination": *ENW*, 534–5.

P. 75. Westchester County: M. Folsom in *New York Times*, December 23, 1961.

P. 76. Ground water supplies: *Clebsch and Lieberman*, 307.

P. 76. Second footnote: personal communication with Dr. Gary Higgin, Lawrence Radiation Laboratory.

Pp. 76–7. Jamaica Water Supply: *Jam. Water Supp. Co.*

P. 77. C. K. Shafer: *Holifield*, 52–3.

P. 77. "Approximately 2,500,000 dwelling units": *BFB, NYS*, 30.

P. 77. Window breakage: *ENW*, 73, 108–9, 232.

P. 77. Footnote: *Holifield*, maps opposite pp. 12, 44.

P. 78. "The suburbs . . . eastern Pennsylvania": *Ibid.*

Pp. 78–9. "In addition to . . . human activity": *ARS*, 18.

P. 79. White Oak Lake study: *Auerbach 1961*, 340–2 (citing Crossley).

P. 80. "Detailed analysis . . . in 1961": *Auerbach 1961*, 338 (citing Neel and Larson).

P. 80. Marine cycling (second paragraph): *Schaefer et al.*

P. 80. Radioisotopes in Marshall Islands: *Seymour*, 355–6.

Pp. 80–1. Islanders' body burden: *Conard et al. 1962*, 42–3.

P. 81. "For example, . . . serious hazards": *Comar*, 342–3.

P. 81. Ralph Lapp: *Lapp 1961*.

P. 81. Federal Radiation Laboratory report: *New York Times*, June 2, 1963.

P. 82. Bone contamination in U.S. and second footnote: *Kulp and Schulert*, 624.

P. 82. Derivation of barium 140: *Grummitt*, 377.

P. 82. Radiocesium: *Langham*, 519; E. C. Anderson et al., fig. 13, p. 507.

P. 82. First footnote (derivation of calcium and strontium): *ARS*, fig. 12, p. 26.

P. 83. Footnote: *UN 1962*, paragraph 403, p. 160.

Pp. 83–4. Land-restoration suggestions: *ARS*, 28–33.

P. 84. Other investigators: *Auerbach 1962*, 329.

P. 84. Work animals and windmills: *Stat. Abs. 1962*, table 713, p. 528.

CHAPTER 8

P. 86. Leontief: *Leontief and Hoffenberg*, 48.

P. 86. Melman: *Melman 1961*.

P. 87. New York City statistics: *BFB, NYC*, 2–14.

P. 88. Blast-induced deaths: *Holifield Civil Defense 1961*, 213.
P. 88. 1,446-megaton attack: *Holifield*, 12, 847, 853.
P. 88. Iklé: *Iklé 1958*, 27.
P. 88. Hoegh: *Holifield Civil Defense 1960*, 118.
P. 89. New York City transportation statistics: *BFB, NYC*, 2–14.
P. 89. Destruction of transportation equipment: *ENW*, 108–9, 173–6, 254–5.
P. 89. Motor vehicles in New York City: *Winkler*, 31.
P. 89. Destruction of ships: *ENW*, 108–9, 176–8.
P. 89. Power requirements: *Stat. Abs. 1962*, table 712, p. 528.
P. 90. Germany: *SBSb*, 148, 162.
Pp. 90–1. S. G. Winter: *Holifield Civil Defense 1961*, 308, 312–13, 326–8.
Pp. 91–2. Hachiya: *Hachiya*, 87, 117, 133, 144, 193, 196, 214, 215.
P. 92. Hiroshima population increase: *Nordlie and Popper* (citing Trumbull 1957).
P. 92. Role conflicts: *Nordlie and Popper*, 33–4.
P. 93. Banfield study: *Banfield*.
P. 94. Black Death: *Langer*, 295.
P. 94. Koreans: *Busch*, 111.
P. 94. London fire: *Leasor*, 228–31, 272–3.
P. 94. American refugees: *Collins*, 74, 130, 135–6.
Pp. 94–5. London plague: *Leasor*, 113–14.
P. 95. Nevada: UPI dispatch in *Los Angeles Herald Express*, July 28, 1961.

CHAPTER 9

P. 96. Footnote: *MEJ*, 3, 448, 450–8.
Pp. 96–7. Holifield-attack estimates: *Holifield*, 852, 853.
Pp. 97–8. "Many of these . . . epidemic diseases": *Stowman 1946*, 324–5.
P. 98. Influenza pandemic: *Shope 1944*, 418.
P. 98. Germans: *SBSa*, 263.
P. 98. Typhus in Germany: *Stowman 1945*, 295.
P. 99. Description of typhus fever: *Anderson and Arnstein*, 449–50.
P. 99. Typhus fever in World Wars I and II: *Stowman 1945*, 289–310.
Pp. 99–100. Typhus in Naples: *Wheeler*.
P. 100. Typhus in Germany: *Stowman 1945*, 293–6; *Stowman 1946*, 415.
P. 100. Description of dysentery: *Smillie*, 246.
P. 101. Dysentery in U.S.: *Stat. Abs. 1962*, 84; *Nagan*.
P. 101. Entameba histolytica: *Anderson and Arnstein*, 188.
P. 101. Third paragraph: *Thale and Opper*, 1150.
P. 101. Fourth paragraph: *Hollis and Fellton*, 1433.
P. 102. Dysentery and typhoid in Berlin: *Stowman 1946*, 415.
Pp. 102–3. Tularemia ("An interesting . . . of these animals" and footnote): *Gelman*, 97–100; *Schmidt*.
P. 103. Horseflies and deerflies: *Bishopp and Philip*, 151.
P. 103. Tularemia in U.S.: *Stat. Abs. 1962*, 84.
P. 104. Description of plague (*Pasteurella pestis*): *Hirst*, 197, 310–20, 461.
P. 104. Plague in U.S.: *Anderson and Arnstein*, 299.
P. 104. Bubonic plague: *Hirst*, 459, 463.

Pp. 104–5. Pneumonic plague (to "100 per cent"): *Wu,* 20, 27, 34.

P. 105. Drugs: *Zinsser,* 464–5.

P. 105. Deaths in 1961: U.S. Public Health Service announcement, August 3, 1963.

P. 105. Plague in U.S. (to "being permanent"): *Eskey and Haas,* 1–24; *PHR.*

P. 106. "This would require . . . plague bacilli": *Pollitzer and Meyer,* 473.

Pp. 106–7. San Francisco epidemic: *Link,* 12–13, 20.

P. 107. Outbreak in Oakland: *Eskey and Haas,* 2.

Pp. 107–8. Outbreak in Manchuria: *Wu,* 4–5, 33.

CHAPTER 10

P. 112. Hiroshima (lines 6–10): *Hollingsworth.*

P. 112. "Other studies . . . times as great": *NAS 1961b,* 19 (citing Lewis 1957 and Hemplemann 1960).

P. 112. "Prenatal X-ray . . . per cent": *MacMahon.*

Pp. 112–13. Hiroshima Medical Association: *Harada and Ishida,* 1261–3.

P. 113. Changes in the blood system: *NAS 1961b,* 28–30.

P. 113. Marshall Islanders: *Conard et al. 1962,* 26–34, 45.

P. 113. Rats and mice: *NAS 1961b,* 28–30.

Pp. 113–14. "A small . . . seven cells": *Brewen.*

P. 113. Quote in footnote: *UN 1962,* paragraph 22, p. 43.

P. 114. "One hundred roentgens . . . following high doses": *Puck et al.*

Pp. 114–15. "A person may . . . infectious diseases": *NAS 1961b,* 3–9.

P. 115. Death rate: *Holifield,* 592, 602, 603.

P. 115. Cataracts (to "is not clear"): *NAS 1961b,* 20–3.

P. 115. Last sentence: *Hollingsworth,* 486 (citing Miller 1956).

P. 116. First two paragraphs: *NAS 1961b,* 23–7.

P. 116. Reactor operators: *Grahn.*

Pp. 116–17. "In females . . . would in adults": *NAS 1961b,* 23–7.

P. 117. Mammalian embryos: *Rugh.*

P. 117. Microcephaly: *Hollingsworth,* 485.

Pp. 117–18. "In addition to . . . abnormal termination": *MEJ,* 162–3.

P. 118. Exposed Marshall Islanders: *Conard et al. 1962,* 44.

P. 118. Japanese children; *NAS 1961b,* 28.

P. 118. Marshall Islanders: *Conard et al. 1962,* fig. 12, p. 18.

Pp. 118–19. Marshall Islands boys and girls: *Ibid.,* table 9, p. 21.

P. 119. First footnote: *Ibid.,* 1.

CHAPTER 11

Pp. 121–2. Columbia River, Hanford Plant: *Odum,* 468–9.

P. 122. Radiophosphorus damage: *Stonier 1956.*

P. 122. White Oak Lake Bed: *Dunaway and Kay.*

P. 122. Radiation as stress: Personal communication with R. B. Platt.

P. 123. The first variable (entire paragraph): *Gustafsson,* table 1, p. 176; *Gunckel and Sparrow,* 563; *Strehler,* 134, 137; *Spector,* 471; *Bletchly and Fisher; Cornwell, Crook, and Bull; King, Darrow, and Kaye; Myers and Drobkin.*

P. 124. Fruit-fly studies in Marshall Islands: Wheeler et al. in *Stone et al.,* 261-3.

Pp. 124–5. Plant studies: *Fosberg;* Blumberg and Conard in *Conard et al. 1961,* 85–6.

P. 125. Vertebrates: *Cronkite et al.,* 76–9.

P. 126. Tillamook forest fire: *Keen 1952,* 693.

Pp. 126–7. Engelmann spruce bark beetles: *Wygant and Nelson,* 417–19; *Keen 1952,* 688.

P. 127. Woodwell: *Woodwell 1962,* figs. 3–5 and pp. 574–6.

P. 128. 500 to 1: *Keen 1949,* 429.

P. 28. Spruce budworm: *Morris et al.*

P. 128. Engelmann spruce bark beetles: *Wygant and Nelson,* 419.

Pp. 128–9: Burks quote: *Burks,* 374.

P. 129. "Even mites ... species": *Rhode,* 575–6.

Pp. 129–30. Birds (to "and even coyotes"): *Kalmbach,* 726–9.

P. 131. Predator and prey mites: *Auerbach 1958; Rhode,* 577.

P. 131. DDT: *Elton,* 151.

P. 131. Locusts: *Odum,* 196–7.

Pp. 131–2. Crowding: *Steinhaus.*

P. 132. Swedish scientists: *Simak and Gustafsson,* 464–5.

P. 132. "Insects influence . . . to disease attack": *Black,* 22–6; *Leach,* 63–7.

P. 133. Dutch elm disease: *Gravatt and Parker.*

P. 133. *Xylosandrus germanus: Elton,* 72.

P. 133. *Endoconidiophora fagacaerum: Bretz,* 851–5.

P. 133. Dutch elm disease (synergistic effect): *Gravatt and Parker,* 447.

P. 133. Gypsy moth: *Corliss,* 695.

P. 133. 5,000 roentgens: *Gunckel and Sparrow,* 569.

P. 134. Loblolly pines: *Pedigo.*

P. 134. "Spruce seeds . . . 1,000 roentgens": *Simak and Gustafsson,* 465–6.

P. 134. "Most herbaceous plants . . . than are trees": *Woodwell in prep.*

CHAPTER 12

P. 136. Dirt particles: *Biel,* 334.

P. 136. Colorado: personal communication with Dr. C. Kearny, The Hudson Institute.

P. 137. "Particles in . . . rain and snow": *Fletcher,* 48–102, 210–58, 293–308, 327–47.

P. 137. Colonel Lunger: *Holifield,* 839.

P. 137. Footnote (dimensions of crater): *ENW 1962,* 289, 292–3.

Pp. 137–8. Krakatoa and Tomboro eruptions: *Humphreys 1940,* 603, 611–15; *Ingersoll; Wexler,* 96.

Pp. 138–9. Footnote: *Wexler,* 95, 96.

Pp. 138–9. Humphreys (up to "cover the earth"): *Humphreys 1940,* 600; *Humphreys 1929,* 579, 585.

P. 139. Material gouged out of the ground: *ENW 1962,* 289, 292–3.

P. 140. Ayres: *Ayres.*

P. 140. New York weather: *New York Weather Almanac.*

P. 140. "Whereas water . . . 85 per cent": *Wexler,* 94.

P. 140. Humphreys: *Humphreys 1940,* 631–2.

P. 140. Footnote: *Biel,* 328.

P. 142. Platt: *Platt,* 25.

P. 142. Tobacco plant: *Braun.*

P. 142. Eniwetok: *Palumbo.*

P. 143. 25,000-acre tract: *Neiland, 660.*

P. 143. "Certain plants . . . sensititve plants": *McCormick and Platt.*

P. 143. "This process . . . with erosion": *Sears, 94.*

P. 143. Shoot meristems: *Sparrow and Woodwell, 15.*

P. 143. Footnote: *Holifield Civil Defense 1961, 354.*

Pp. 143–4. "Terrestrial plant . . . climax fauna": *Benton and Werner,* Ch. 5.

P. 144. Benton and Werner: *Ibid., 119.*

Pp. 144–5. Ore-smelting towns: *Mitchell,* 13 (citing Hursh 1948); *Daubenmire,* fig. 56, p. 252.

P. 145. North Africa: *Lowdermilk 1953; Bouillene.*

P. 146. Rain forests: *Bouillene.*

P. 146. Hedges in Germany: *Elton,* 157 (citing Hartke and Marquardt).

P. 146. Shelter belts: *Stoeckeler, 3–4.*

P. 146. Canopy of trees: *Selleck and Schupper.*

Pp. 146–7. Tillamook: *Neiland.*

P. 147. "The difference . . . 25° hotter": *Daubenmire, 164–5.*

P. 147. "In winter . . . conductivity": *Biel, 329, 334.*

P. 147. Grasshoppers and rabbits: *Odum,* 196–7, 446; *Milne and Milne,* 177.

P. 147. Overgrazing: *Weaver, 75–6.*

P. 147. "It is not . . . desert community": *Odum, 269.*

Pp. 147–8. Holland and Australia: *Milne and Milne, 176.*

P. 148. Sears quote: *Sears, 98.*

P. 148. May 1934: H. H. Bennett, Director of the Interior Department's Soil Erosion Service, quoted in the *New York Times,* May 14, 1934.

P. 148. Footnote: *Stoeckeler, 9.*

P. 149. Dust bowl not irreversible: *Mitchell, 14–17.*

P. 149. Israel and Huleh Basin: *Lowdermilk 1960.*

P. 150. "At first . . . land upstream": *Sears, 100.*

P. 150. "The extent . . . cover": personal communication with F. H. Bormann.

Pp. 150–1. "Hundred dead cities": *Lowdermilk 1953, 10.*

P. 151. "The Syrian . . . Illinois": *World Almanac; Stat. Abs.*

P. 151. Footnote: *Oosting, 320–2.*

Pp. 151–2. U.S. climate: personal communication with E. R. Biel; *Biel,* 332, 345, 351.

P. 152. Clouds over deserts: *Fletcher, 119–21.*

P. 152. Mesopotamia: *Fisher,* 86–9, 121, 138–9; *Coke,* 148, 153–4; *Christen.*

P. 152. Footnote: *Geiger, 309–16.*

CHAPTER 13

P. 153. 25,000,000,000,000 cells: *King, 65.*

P. 154. Forty-six chromosomes: *Ibid., 164.*

Pp. 154–5. Genetic four-letter alphabet: *Crick; Nirenberg.*

P. 155. "A number . . . in a hundred": *UN 1962,* paragraph 64, p. 90; paragraph 154, p. 101.

P. 155. Muller: *Muller.*
P. 155. Background radiation: *Gentry, Parkhurst, and Bulin; Beardsley.*
Pp. 155–6. Discussion of when a gene is harmful: *Wright; Dobzhansky 1961.*
P. 156. 30 roentgens, 120 roentgens: *UN 1962*, paragraph 154, p. 101.
P. 156. Population A: *Holifield*, 592.
P. 156. Population B: *Ibid.*, 858.
P. 156. First footnote ("genetic polymorphism"): *Allison.*
P. 157. Pregnancy terminations and infant deaths: Yerushalmy in *WHO*, iii.
P. 157. Wallace and Dobzhansky: *Wallace and Dobzhansky*, 174–7.
P. 157. UN: *UN 1962*, paragraph 154, p. 101.
P. 157. Dubinin: Dubinin as quoted personally by Dobzhansky.
P. 157. Other geneticists: *Neel and Schull*, 211–12 (citing Haldane and Westergaard).
P. 158. Muller: *Muller.*
P. 159. Swedish scientists: *Lüning et al.*
P. 159. Japanese populations: *Schull and Neel 1958.*
P. 159. Wallace and Dobzhansky: *Wallace and Dobzhansky*, 187.
Pp. 159–61. Langer on Black Death: *Langer*, 292–303.
P. 161. Banfield: *Banfield.*
P. 161. Footnote: *McDowell*, 4; *Trevelyan 1937*, 591.
P. 162. "In 1841 . . . the population": *McDowell*, 4–5.
P. 162. Blight (lines 9–23): *O'Neill*, 209–11.
P. 162. Public aid: *Nowlan*, 204.
P. 162. Next-to-last paragraph: *Edwards and Williams*, Chs. 4, 5, 7.
Pp. 162–3. Census of 1851: *MacArthur*, 308–12.
P. 163. "These losses . . . Australia": *MacDonagh*, 322–8, 388.
P. 163. Population decline (lines 8–32): *O'Brien*, 13, 16, 17, 19, 23, 33.
P. 164. "On the other . . . from the past": *McHugh*, 396, 417–21, 434–5.
Pp. 164–5. MacDonagh: *MacDonagh*, 329.
P. 165. Waste of potatoes (lines 6–11): *McHugh*, 395–7.
P. 165. Marriage (lines 12–19): *Murray*, 78–9.
P. 165. Sheridan: *Sheridan*, 190.
P. 166. Langer: *Langer*, 292.
P. 167. Huxley and Miller: *Huxley; Miller.*
P. 168. Mesopotamia: for an excellent study of the destruction of Mesopotamia, see *Christen.*

INDEX

TOM STONIER took his doctorate at Yale. He has been on the staff of The Rockefeller Institute and is now engaged in biological research at Manhattan College. Portions of this book are based on a report—entitled *The Anticipated Biological and Environmental Effects of Detonating a 20-Megaton Weapon on Columbus Circle*—prepared for the Scientists' Committee for Radiation Information and presented to the New York Academy of Sciences. Dr. Stonier has lectured on the effects of nuclear weapons to many scientific, medical, educational, community, and other groups, including the American Association for the Advancement of Science and the New York and Washington Academies of Sciences.

GERARD PIEL is the publisher and editor of *Scientific American*. He has contributed numerous articles to magazines and is the author of *Science in the Cause of Man*. In 1963 he was awarded the Kalinga Prize for his contributions to science education.